Penguin Books
Sunday Times Brain Teasers

Sunday Times Brain Teasers

Edited by Ronald Postill

With illustrations by
Charlie Riddell

Penguin Books

Penguin Books Ltd, Harmondsworth,
Middlesex, England
Penguin Books Inc., 7110 Ambassador Road,
Baltimore, Maryland 21207, U.S.A.
Penguin Books Australia Ltd, Ringwood,
Victoria, Australia
Penguin Books Canada Ltd,
41 Steelcase Road West, Markham, Ontario, Canada

First published 1974
Problems 1–90 published in *The Sunday Times*
copyright © Times Newspapers Ltd, 1962–73
This edition copyright © Penguin Books, 1974

Made and printed in Great Britain by
Hazell Watson & Viney Ltd,
Aylesbury, Bucks
Set in Monotype Times

Contents

The Sunday Times
Brain Teaser

The Sunday Times Brain Teaser was introduced in the 1950s. It was included with other puzzles and competitions usually published at Christmastime. As it grew in popularity it appeared more frequently, in its own right, and on 26 February 1961 it became, with H. Wright's 'Tall Story', a weekly and numbered feature. Number One set the mood since Mr Wright, having asked readers, on scant evidence, for the name, age and height of the tallest of his triplets, observed: 'Any who are stumped at the expiry of an hour should feel cause for concern.' Many were and did.

The Brain Teaser is now firmly established, its elucidation being attempted not only by thousands of readers throughout the United Kingdom but also by competitors in almost sixty overseas states. Published problems all come from readers, the number offered being far beyond the requirement.

What distinguishes the STBT is its unique genre, for although it is the joy of many mathematicians from world-famous professors to eleven-year-olds the true BT is biased to puzzlement, to reasoning and logic, and not to specialized mathematical techniques, and is not concerned with probabilities, transpositions, codes and ciphers. Validity, uniqueness, accurate and justifiable phraseology and short compass are its aims, tempered by two factors: first, that liberties must sometimes be allowed to the puzzler which might be denied to the mathematician and, second, that occasionally a problem should be more easily solved than usual since interest is so wide that some latitude should be allowed for readers of modest mathematical ability.

It follows that when latitude is allowed the number of solvers increases by three to four times from an average of perhaps one thousand a week, whereas, when the blend of maths and mystery is potent, entries, as distinct from efforts, are often down to a handful.

It has been estimated that in any year at least a hundred thousand readers may well try successfully or otherwise to solve problems. Of these, the ratio of women to men competitors has in the past ten years risen from one in ten to one in five, though only three women have so far composed problems acceptable for publication.

Inevitably a considerable correspondence ensues, either paying tribute or, usually recklessly, exposing some ambiguity or departure from the unique. And since space allows only the final answer, there is frequently a despairing call for the full progressive solution.

Special appreciation of a particularly brilliant problem is usually confined to one or two words on the entry postcard but more often can be sensed by the surge of entries from new competitors or by requests for the solution long after publication of the puzzle.

Perhaps the most outstanding example of teasing is Brain Teaser 186, of 15 November 1964, which was based on a deceptively simple diagram by an undergraduate, Adrian Winder, who died in a road accident just before his puzzle was published. Few correct answers were submitted; within the year there were 250 requests for the full solution; and still, from time to time, yet another reader concedes defeat and begs to be relieved of his misery.

Mr Winder's problem, with his solution, is published as a fitting postscript to this collection.

ANTHONY FRENCH

Introduction

Ten of the most prolific Brain Teaser composers were invited to contribute to this book. It follows that many excellent puzzles from occasional setters are not included, which is a pity; perhaps one of their number will be encouraged to produce Volume 2.

The first ninety problems have appeared in the *Sunday Times* (though a few have been slightly modified to remove possible ambiguity or to replace outmoded currency). Thanks are due to the *Sunday Times* for permission to reprint. They are arranged in groups of ten, one from each setter in alphabetical order; thus, Nos. 1, 11, 21 . . . are by J.L.B., Nos. 2, 12, 22 . . . are by G.H.D. and so on.

Problems 91 to 100 appear for the first time; there is one from each of us, but they are arranged in haphazard order so as to produce Brain Teaser 101 – Spot the Setter. (A key, providing the solution to 101, appears at the end.)

As solvers may be interested to know something of their tormentors, here are brief biographies. There is ample evidence to suggest that some who attempt the *Sunday Times* problems get as much enjoyment from catching out the setter in some error as from *solving* the thing. They will no doubt address their complaints to the appropriate sinner, c/o Penguin Books.

1. J. L. BOWLES

Retired Insurance Official associated, from 1923 to 1963, with the Overseas Department in London of a prominent Group of Insurance Companies. Lives in Gloucestershire and occupies his leisure with golf, cricket, puzzles and crosswords.

2. G. H. DICKSON

Formerly President of I.C.I. (Japan) Ltd. and later, on retirement to Ireland, an executive of the Confederation of Irish Industry.

Now divides his time between shrub-gardening and chasing the wily trout amid the scenic beauty of Co. Donegal.

3. E. R. EMMET

Assistant Master at Winchester College 1932–63, 1965–72, and Housemaster 1947–63. Author of several books on logic, economics, and philosophy, and of collections of puzzles. His Nos. 13 and 23 appeared in *101 Brain Puzzlers* (Macmillan), published by Emerson in U.S.A. as *Brain Puzzler's Delight*; No. 3 appeared in *Learning to Think* (Longmans); Nos. 3 and 33 were in *Puzzles for Pleasure* (Emerson).

4. BRIGADIER W. M. GREENWAY

On retirement from the Royal Artillery, renewed his interest in mathematics by teaching at St Paul's School, and now lectures at the Royal Military Academy. Spends his spare time on the easier jobs of farm maintenance, furniture repair and manufacture, and woodwork. On rare occasions plays golf or bridge.

5. SIR JAMES JOINT

Retired after forty years in the Diplomatic Service. Lectures on Latin-American affairs, and fiddles with clocks and watches.

6. R. POSTILL

Headmaster of Victoria College, Jersey, 1946–67; now Tutor for Admissions at Millfield School. Interested in anything cryptic (e.g. crosswords and cricket). Performs the more menial tasks in the garden with ill-concealed distaste.

7. C. SKEFFINGTON QUIN

After early years in South Africa, trained as an Army Schoolmaster at the Duke of York's Royal Military School. Served at Ypres and on the Somme with the Worcestershire Regiment. District Military Education Officer in Baluchistan and, later, in Chatham. Retired to cultivate his garden and devise puzzles.

8. J. S. ROWLEY

Formerly Head of the Mathematics Department of Victoria College, Jersey. Retired, he occupies himself with choral music and gardening (though seldom simultaneously).

9. W. A. THATCHER

Managing Director of a rubber-moulding company. Formerly a mathematician at the Air Ministry and with Rolls-Royce; for a time a Headmaster. Plays bridge and chess.

10. B. W. M. YOUNG

Read Classics at Cambridge and is therefore a naïve mathematician. For twelve years Headmaster of Charterhouse and for six years Director of the Nuffield Foundation. Now Director-General of the Independent Broadcasting Authority. Has composed chess problems, but finds the making of Brain Teasers a more convenient diversion if conferences become dull.

The *Eleventh Man* is Anthony French, Brain Teaser Editor of the *Sunday Times*, author of that admirable book on the First World War, *Gone for a Soldier* (The Roundwood Press). He has unearthed puzzles which we had mislaid; no less important, he has helped us to recall their solutions. In dedicating this miscellany to him we ask his forgiveness for its imperfections, which would have been far more numerous but for his guidance.

R. POSTILL

Problems

1

Absentees

Only seven men still had ammunition. Aden had 1 round, Bill 2, Cuff 3, Dudd 4, Edge 5, Ford 6 and Good 7.

The Commander ordered that there should always be five of the seven men on duty and that the duty roster should be so arranged that those on duty never had fewer than 17 rounds of ammunition.

Next day he was told that only four men were on duty. It appeared that three of the five who should have been present were sick and that the four doing duty included two who should have been off. It so happened that the four had between them the same number of rounds as the five would have had.

The Commander had no copy of the duty roster, but he knew how many rounds each of the seven men had. He asked how many rounds the four men doing duty had between them and, when told, said, after some thought, that he knew with certainty who the three absentees were.

Who were they?

2

South Pacific

Among those innumerable South Pacific islands in which the vicinity of longitude 180° abounds, there are three neighbouring ones between which an ancient ferry-boat maintains each week a regular schedule. This schedule, which is strictly adhered to except when ordered otherwise, is:

ALOHA	dep.	Monday	9 a.m.
BALI-HAI	arr.	Tuesday	7 p.m.
BALI-HAI	dep.	Tuesday	10 p.m.
CRACKATOEA	arr.	Friday	9 p.m.
CRACKATOEA	dep.	Saturday	7 a.m.
ALOHA	arr.	Sunday	7 p.m.

The ferry maintains the same leisurely speed throughout each leg of the triangular circuit.

The Port Authority at the home port of Aloha, one Thursday at 9 p.m., radioed to the ferry on its course between the other two islands that a hurricane in the area was imminent, and ordered it to proceed at once to the nearest of the three for shelter.

Without altering speed, the captain immediately complied.

Which island did he accordingly reach, and what were the day and hour of his arrival there?

3

The Pay Roll Rules

I am the Managing Director of a factory and I have under me five employees. Their names are Alf, Bert, Charlie, Duggie and Ernie, and their jobs are, not necessarily respectively, Doorkeeper, Doorknob Polisher, Bottle Washer, Welfare Office and Worker.

There has been some dissatisfaction recently about wages which in the past, I am bound to admit, have sometimes been rather haphazard. It is clearly very difficult to arrange things in such a way that merit is appropriately rewarded, but it seemed to me important that everybody's position should at least be clear. After much thought, therefore, I put up the following notice:

WAGES

1. Alf is to get more than Duggie.
2. Ernie is to get 12 per cent more than the Bottle Washer will when he receives the 10 per cent rise that he will be getting next month.
3. The Doorknob Polisher is to get 30 per cent more than he used to.
4. Charlie is to get £12 a year less than 20 per cent more than the Welfare Officer.
5. No one is to get less than £200 or more than £600 a year.
6. The Doorkeeper is to get 5 per cent more than he would if he got 10 per cent less than Bert.

Everyone always has received in my Factory, receives now, and as long as I am in charge always will receive an exact number of £s per year.

What are the various jobs of my employees and what yearly wage is each of them to get?

4

Towns and Families

Cardiff and London share a line of latitude; Cardiff and Edinburgh share a line of longitude.

The Archers, the Brewers, the Carters and the Drews are four married couples born and married in London, Cardiff, Edinburgh and Belfast. One of each sex was born in each city; one marriage took place in each city. No one was married in the city of his or her birth. Mrs Archer was the only woman married east of where she was born; Mr Archer was the only man married south of where he was born; Mr Brewer was the only man to marry a woman born north of him. Mr Carter and Mrs Drew were twins.

Where were the Carters married?

5

Book Pages

A famous book by Brian Teezer has eight chapters, each starting on a right-hand page. All the chapters except one have a half-page of footnotes, which are printed separately after each chapter.

Each chapter has one more page than the preceding chapter, the last chapter having fewer than 30 pages.

The current edition of the book contains 200 pages, but the printer has pointed out that when a reprint is issued he can save four pages by assembling all the footnotes at the end of Chapter 8.

How many completely blank pages are there in the current edition and how many will there be in the reprint?

6

Batting Averages

Allen and Biggin, stalwarts of our village cricket side, have an annual wager: whichever finishes the season with the lower batting average buys the other a dinner.

Last season the result was in doubt until the last ball of the last match, when Allen (offering no stroke) was adjudged 'out' leg-before-wicket. Had he been given 'not out' (which, incidentally, would have been the first 'not-out' innings either had played) his batting average – a whole number – would have beaten Biggin's by exactly 0·5 of a run. In the event Biggin won by exactly 0·5 of a run.

Both players comfortably passed a season's total of 300 runs but neither reached 500. Biggin had three fewer innings than Allen.

How many runs did Biggin score during the season?

Note for the non-cricketer: batting average is calculated by dividing a player's total runs by his number of completed innings, i.e. times 'out'.

7

Which Page?

A student, desiring to find a reference in a book, could not remember the actual page number, but only the three figures it comprises.

Before beginning his search, he wrote down in ascending order the six possible variants of the three figures. In writing the second variant his pencil broke on a figure which thereafter was illegible. With a fresh pencil he completed the list of variants and then found his reference, the page number being in fact the second variant.

Some time later he found in his pocket the scrap of paper bearing the six numbers. Idly adding them, he obtained a total of 4796, having unwittingly misread the illegible figure.

On what page was the reference?

8

House-Number

I live in a long street in which the houses are all on one side numbered consecutively.

If I add my house-number to the sum of a certain number of consecutive house-numbers on my immediate left, the answer is equal to the sum of the same number of consecutive house-numbers on my immediate right.

Moreover, if I add the square of my house-number to the sum of the squares of a different number of consecutive house-numbers on my immediate left, the result is equal to the sum of the squares of the same number of consecutive house-numbers on my immediate right.

I do not live at number 12, and perhaps I should add that my house-number is less than 14,000.

What is it?

9

Electing a Chairman

The ten directors of the Everlasting Mutual Trust Company, Chairman (C), Secretary (S), Treasurer (T), Directors 1, 2, 3, 4, 5, 6, and Vice-Chairman (V), sat in that order to elect a new chairman.

They all got one vote. No director voted for himself, or for his neighbour, or for the man who voted for him. No officer voted for an officer. C voted for the man who voted for the man who voted for 2, i.e. C vote vote vote 2 for short; and T vote vote vote 4 and V vote vote vote 5 and S vote vote vote 6. Director 4 did not vote for an officer. Neither C nor S voted for 3. The man getting a vote from 6 did not vote for 3.

For whom did C, S, T, 1, 2, 3, 4, 5, 6, V respectively vote?

10
Brothers and Sisters

The boys and girls of a primary school have recently done a survey among themselves. They find that half the children who have brothers are girls who have no sisters, and that half the children who have sisters are girls who have no brothers. Boys who have no sisters are equal in number to boys who have sisters but not brothers. In all, there are fourteen more children with sisters than there are children with brothers.

How many of the boys have neither sisters nor brothers?

11

Club Lockers

The lockers in one section of the new club-house are numbered 1 to 12 consecutively. Last Saturday, Pitcher arrived without his key. He was surprised to find that his locker could be opened by the key to Putter's locker which is next to his.

Pitcher at once saw Wedge, the secretary, and Bunker, the captain. From them he learned that there are only three different key patterns for the twelve lockers (patterns A, B, and C) and that the total of the numbers on the four A lockers is the same as the corresponding total for the four B lockers, which is the same as that for the four C lockers.

Wedge also told Pitcher that no two lockers with pattern A keys are adjoining. He added that his own key is of the same pattern as Wood's and that the total of the numbers on Wood's and Wedge's lockers is sixteen. He further mentioned that of the three lockers, other than the captain's own locker, which can be opened by the captain's key, the nearest to the captain's locker is further from the captain's locker than are five (but not more) lockers which cannot be opened by the captain's key.

By this time, Pitcher was making for the wall; but if the number on Putter's locker is higher than the number on Wedge's locker . . .

What is the number on Bunker's locker ?

12

Hymn Numbers

The hymn-board in church was electrically operated and made provision for any four hymn numbers of up to three digits in each (from 0 to 9), but did not provide any blanks so that Hymn No. 7 for example would appear on the board as 007 and No. 77 as 077.

One Sunday a parishioner noticed with surprise that not only was each of the four hymn numbers for that service a perfect square, but moreover each of the three numbers produced in the vertical columns was a four-digit perfect square.

When, back home, he told his son Tom of this unique occurrence, the latter exclaimed, 'I can't believe it! What were the numbers then?', to which the father replied, 'You already know enough to work that out for yourself, but it will be of help to you to learn that I also noticed that the totals of the digits of each hymn number were perfect squares too and that, coincidentally, one of these squares would result from dividing the final hymn number into the figure in the middle column.'

But Tom still couldn't puzzle it out and demanded to be told at any rate one of the hymn numbers, to which his father responded, 'All I can remember now is that the third hymn number ended in two noughts.'

What was the opening hymn number?

13

Our Factory on the Cricket Field

We are all keen and most of us active cricketers. In one of our tea breaks the other day, Alf, Bert, Charlie, Duggie and Ernie were discussing their last match. Four of them had been playing for the factory side, and one had been umpiring. Of the four players one was an opening bat (who did not bowl), one the wicket-keeper (who also of course did not bowl), one a fast bowler, and the other a leg-break bowler. It was a one-innings match in which no individual scored more than 100 runs.

The umpire of course always tells the truth, and so does the wicket-keeper. The leg-break bowler has been trained in the ways of deception and never tells the truth, the fast bowler and the opening batsman make statements which are alternately true and false, or false and true.

They speak as follows:

ALF: 1. Ernie is not the leg-break bowler.
        2. Charlie's score is not a multiple of 9.
        3. Two of the opposition were run out.

BERT: 1. Charlie's score was a multiple of 7.
        2. Duggie scored twice as many as Alf and Bert between them.
        3. Duggie scored 10 per cent more than Charlie.

CHARLIE: 1. The fast bowler and the leg-break bowler took the same number of wickets.
         2. Duggie's score was a perfect square.

DUGGIE: 1. Charlie took 4 wickets.
        2. Charlie scored less than Bert.
        3. Ernie took 5 wickets.

4. I scored exactly as many as two of the others between them.
5. Alf was the wicket-keeper.

ERNIE: 1. Duggie was not the umpire.
        2. Duggie took more than 3 wickets.
        3. Alf scored 37.
        4. Bert scored 8 times as many runs as the fast bowler
           took wickets.

*Who did what, and how many runs and wickets, if any, did each of
them get?*

14

Midsummer Birthday Madness

Midsummer Day 1962 (24 June) was my youngest grandson John's first birthday, and I was then able to claim that my nine grandchildren were aged 0, 1, 2, 3, 4, 5, 6, 7 and 8 years old (neglecting, of course, the odd days). They were all born in June, and if they are arranged in date order, the following facts are true: John is the middle grandchild; the sum of the dates of the last four is an exact multiple of the sum of the dates of the first four; the sum of the ages of the last four is two thirds of the sum of the ages of the first four; the sum of the years of birth of the first three is equal to the sum of the years of birth of the last three. The intervals between birthdays are 0, 1, 2, 3, 4, 5, 6 and 7 days, but not in that order.

My eldest son's two daughters are exactly two years apart; the twins were born four hours apart; two children are as old as their dates of birth.

What was the date of birth of the grandchild born in 1954?

15

Electric Clock

My watch keeps perfect time and so does my electric wall clock until the battery starts to run down. I check the clock every noon, and when I find that it has lost a minute in 24 hours I know that it will slow down by an additional minute each day until the battery is exhausted.

At noon on a day towards the end of August, when I was preparing for a fortnight's holiday, I noticed that the clock was one minute slow but I forgot to do anything about it. As I hurried off to catch my train at noon on 1 September, I saw that the clock was exactly 21 minutes slow. I put it right and left it at that.

Family matters forced me to return earlier than I had expected, and on my arrival home I found that the clock was still going. I then noticed that the hands of my watch were exactly overlapping, while the hands of the clock were almost so.

It took me a minute to fix a new battery and I at once put the clock on the correct time. In doing so the hands crossed each other three times.

On what date did I return from my holiday?

16

Common Frontier

The adjoining countries of Europhalia and Sopiculia have different standard units of weight and length, but both use the normal units of time. Although both countries use Arabic numerals, neither uses the denary (tens) method of counting, but each has a different integer less than ten as its counting-base.

In reply to my request for more information a Europhalian friend wrote: 'Our unit of weight is the Elbo, and there are 42 Elbos to their 24 Solbos. The length of our common frontier is 21 Emils.' My Sopiculian correspondent replied: '16 Solbos weigh the same as 26 Elbos; the common frontier is 21 Somils long.'

I later discovered that in both countries there is a speed-limit equivalent to our 50 m.p.h. In Sopiculia this is defined by law as 104 Somils per hour.

What is the Europhalian speed-limit?

17

Antics

All distances and dimensions are exact feet; all times, exact seconds; all the spiders run at 5 feet per second; and drop with a maximum fall of 30 feet.

Ara and Chne sat hungry in the top north-west corner of the palace corridor (no flies).

'Could be an ant or two in that bottom south-east corner by the garden door,' said Chne.

'True,' said Ara. She dropped to the floor and headed straight for the prospective meal, while Chne (she never drops) instantly ran down the shortest route via north wall and floor.

Farther along the corridor, Taran and Tula sat hungry together at the top of the south wall.

'Hey, look!' cried Taran, as the ant-hunters approached.

'Must be something in that corner,' said Tula, dropping to the floor and speeding straight toward it.

Taran at the same moment ran direct for the corner. As she started, Ara, clocking 39 seconds, passed by.

Tangle and wrangle! Dead heat all! No ants!

How wide is the corridor?

18

Birthday Party

Some years ago the Bell family were holding their usual annual special birthday party. Four members of the family, of four different generations, had birthdays on the same day of the year. They were old Adam, his son Enoch, Enoch's son Joseph and Joseph's son David. On this occasion David remarked that the sum of any three of their four ages was a perfect square.

Some years later old Adam died on his birthday, but it so happened that on the very same day David's son Samuel was born, and the annual party was continued in subsequent years.

In 1967 at the usual party Samuel made exactly the same remark that David had made on the previous occasion.

In what year did Adam die and how old was he then?

Perhaps I should mention that no one survived to be 100!

19

Space Ship

Says Bell at the pub: 'I've been reading about a space ship. They fly the thing round playing the usual Cops and Robbers stuff, but the way they name the crew is interesting. Using A, B, C, and so on right up to I, no gaps, they make, once only, every possible pair of different letters; so there's no A A, B B and so on, and they take no notice of the order in a pair; so B C's the same as C B.

'Four, including A D and B C, are on a list of officers and on that list no letter appears more than once. All the rest are just proles, but if they have an A initial they call themselves A proles.

'All proles work in shifts with the same number on each shift – not just two shifts; more than that – and at the end of a shift every prole hands over to another whose initials are each one farther on in the alphabet than his own, so A B hands over to B C. Of course, I is followed by A.

'The shifts are picked so that when all shifts have been worked, every prole has been on duty once only.

'Now you tell me who's on the first shift. I want the biggest possible list. Easier than it looks. Usual prize. One pint.'

Which A proles, if any, are on the first shift?

20

Veres and Ficts

Since 1945, when the Veres (who always tell the truth) entered the country of the Ficts (who always lie), there has been a certain amount of intermarriage. So the country now contains four races: the Verifics (children of a Vere father and a Fict mother), who first tell the truth and then lie; the Fivers (children of a Fict father and a Vere mother), who first lie and then tell the truth; the Veres (born of two Vere parents), who are always truthful; and the Ficts (born of two Fict parents), who are always untruthful.

I met four children, one from each race, who told me some interesting things about their sixteen-year-old Prince:

ALAN: The Prince is a Fict. My mother is a sister of the Prince's cook.
BRUCE: The Prince's father is of the same race as Orsino. The Prince's tutor is Carl's grandfather.
CARL: The Prince is of the same race as I am. I am a Verific.
DAVID: Orsino is the Prince's tutor. The Prince's cook is not of the same race as the Prince's father.

What is the race of each child? And what is the race of the Prince?

21

Absorbers

Three men from the Absorbers' Association, three from Bacchante's Bank and three from the Convivial Corporation took a drink together.

From each concern, one man drank sherry, one gin and one whisky. Of the three choosing sherry, one chose medium, one dry and one extra dry. With gin, one took tonic, one lemon and one vermouth. With whisky, one plain water, one soda water and one dry ginger.

The dry sherry drinker did not belong to the same concern as the plain water man nor to the same concern as the vermouth man. The drinkers of dry ginger, lemon and medium sherry were from three different concerns.

Either the tonic man or the plain water man (but not both) was from the Absorbers' Association. The selectors of soda and vermouth were not colleagues, and neither represented Bacchante's Bank.

The tonic man belonged either to the same concern as the dry sherry drinker or to the same concern as the medium sherry man.

Which type of sherry was chosen by a Convivial Corporation man and what did the other men from that same concern take with their gin and their whisky?

22

Billiard Balls

Bill's job at the billiard ball factory is to check that the weight of each ball is 'dead on' and to reject the occasional ball whose weight is not standard. His only equipment for the purpose is a simple though accurate balance having a sizeable pan on each side but no weights. With the help of this and of what he has learnt from the work study people, Bill invariably does his checking in the least possible number of separate weighings requisite for the particular job in hand.

When Bill returned from the canteen one day, his assistant confessed that he had accidentally dropped one reject ball (whether heavier or lighter than standard he did not know) into a bin containing 14 dozen balls of proper weight, and, since all looked and felt alike, Bill had to reweigh the whole lot in a way which would ensure identification of the reject ball in the minimum number of weighings requisite. He knew before he started that only his fourth weighing would reveal how many balls altogether his programme would necessitate being weighed; in the event, this proved to be exactly 250.

(i) How many weighings were required altogether?
(ii) How many balls were used in the third weighing?

23

Holidays Abroad

My old friends Alf, Bert, Charlie, Duggie and Ernie went with their wives for holidays abroad last year to Andorra, Boulogne, Calais, Dunkirk and Ethiopia. I knew that the names of the five wives were Agnes, Beatrice, Clarissa, Daphne and Ethel, but the only information I had about who was married to whom was that for each pair the names of the husband, the wife and last year's holiday destination all began with different letters.

In conversation with the ladies Beatrice told me that she was not married to Alf, and that she had heard from Ernie that Charlie went to Dunkirk last year.

Daphne, however, firmly informed me that Charlie went to Ethiopia and that Beatrice went to Dunkirk. 'Unlike some people I could mention,' she added darkly, 'Alf always tells the truth.'

Clarissa said that when her husband was asked whether Ethel was married to Charlie he replied, 'No.' She went on to tell me that Duggie went to Boulogne.

Of each of these married couples one member always told the truth and the other never did.

Name each man's wife, and holiday resort.

Rugby Results

At a certain stage in our all-against-all Rugby football competition the table of results read as follows. There had been no matches in which neither side had scored at all.

	Played	Points for	against	Match Points
A	3	13	8	5
B	4	16	10	5
C	4	15	18	4
D	3	5	8	2
E	2	3	8	0

What was the result of the match between A and B?

Note: This problem was set when a try was worth 3 points, a penalty goal 3 points and a converted try 5 points. Match points are on the usual basis of 2 for a win and 1 for a draw.

25

Ups and Downs

In the country of Lud there is a strong feeling about whole numbers. They are either loved, hated or feared. The people are divided into three clans: the Ups, who invariably raise any whole number they get hold of by 25 per cent; the Downs, who reduce it by 25 per cent; and the Levels, who are too scared to make any change. No two members of the same clan would ever pass a number to each other. When I arrived in Lud this situation created a problem.

Each month the plantation needed 300 seedlings from the nearest store and the order was passed through a chain of messengers. The chain always consisted of the same number of men and by stern tradition all three clans took part in the proportions 3:2:1.

In January, my first month in charge, I sent off the usual order as established by the previous manager; but the messengers had changed when he left and I received 76 fewer plants than I had expected. When the same thing happened in February I realized that the chain of messengers must be reorganized. While keeping to the rules I changed two members of the chain.

Each succeeding month I sent off the same order, and by June I had made good the shortfall and had a surplus in hand.

How many extra plants had I after the June delivery?

26

Square Meals

Four married couples – the Ables, Becks, Chuffs and Dunns – almost monopolized the tinned-food stall at our bazaar. Each one of the eight stuck to one type of tin and each bought as many tins as he or she paid in 5p units per tin. (All our tins were priced at 5p or some multiple of 5p.)

Each husband spent £6·00 more than his wife, and no two married couples bought the same number of tins.

Susie spent the same as Mr Dunn. Queenie spent under £1·00. Hugh, Mrs Beck and Mr Chuff together bought as many tins as Tilly, Ruby and Mrs Able. Ernest and Frank together spent as much as Hugh and Mrs Chuff. Tilly spent more than Frank's wife (which made George laugh).

Who is Ernest's wife (both names) and how much did she spend?

27

Here and There

All distances are exact miles, all times exact minutes, all ages exact years. Bill, the twins Sue and Sally, and their parents Sam and Jill, all have their ages used as hour/minute numbers.

One sunny morning the family went by car from their home at Here to spend a fortnight with Jill's sister at There-on-Sea. They started at bill minutes past sue a.m., and averaged 36 m.p.h. Bill reflected, 'Funny thing, all our ages together make the same number of years as the distance in miles from Here to There.'

They reached There at sue minutes to bill a.m. On their arrival Aunt Mary gave a delighted welcome. Her son Tom was just setting off on his bicycle to ride to Here, but he delayed 10 minutes to add his own welcome. He then rode off and maintained a steady 12 m.p.h. except for stops of sam minutes for lunch and sue minutes for tea, safely reaching Here at bill minutes past sally p.m.

How old is his aunt ?

28

Rectangular Blocks

Two rectangular blocks have all their dimensions an exact number of inches, all different.

The sum of the edges of one block is equal to the sum of the edges of the other.

The sum of the areas of all the faces of one block is equal to the sum of the areas of all the faces of the other.

The volumes of the two blocks, however, differ by 140 cubic inches. If the smallest of the six dimensions of the two blocks is 5 inches . . .

What are the dimensions of the two blocks?

29

Blocks

'See these eleven blocks?' says a so-called friend. 'Four of them of 8-inch thickness, two of them of 4-inch, three of 3-inch and two of 1-inch thickness.

'Pile them in a column 51 inches high with a 3-inch block at the bottom so that, remaining in position, individual blocks or combinations of adjacent blocks can be used to measure every thickness in exact inches from 1 inch to 48 inches.'

In what order do they stand?

30

Leanda

The special type of boat which is used for races in the island of Leanda requires eight people, each using sculls, as crew. There are two such boats in each village.

A visiting professor has recently discovered that every man and woman in Leanda has a pull of equal strength, except that in each village there is one man (a Bloo, to use the professor's term) with a much stronger pull than the rest. Trial races discover who he is.

The inhabitants of one village consist of some married couples and one widow; they write to the professor, giving their names, and asking him to draw up crew-lists for their trial races.

The professor replies that two races will be enough for their purposes, and sends them the names of two crews for the first race and two crews for the second race; these crews are so picked that, whatever the results of the races, he will be able to tell which man is the Bloo.

How many of these villagers will find it possible to watch trial-racing from the shore?

31

Nine Holes

The card of the course at Triangle Park Golf Club gives the total length of the first 9 holes as 3,360 yards, par for the individual holes (numbers 1 to 9 respectively) being 5, 4, 5, 4, 3, 4, 4, 3, 5 (total 37).

Closer inspection of the card would show that the lengths of the holes (each a whole number of yards) are such that holes Nos. 1, 2 and 3 could each form a different side of the same right-angled triangle (Triangle A) and that other right-angled triangles could similarly be formed from lengths equal to those of holes Nos. 4, 5 and 6 (B); 7, 8 and 9 (C); 1, 4 and 7 (X); 2, 5 and 8 (Y) and 3, 6 and 9 (Z).

Moreover, the total length of the three holes forming Triangle A, the total length of the three holes forming Triangle B, and the total length of the three holes forming Triangle C could similarly form the three sides of another right-angled triangle (Triangle ABC), while yet another right-angled triangle could similarly be constructed from the total lengths of the holes forming triangles X, Y and Z (Triangle XYZ).

In triangle ABC, the sides would be in the ratio 5:3:4.

The length of each of the par 3 holes is between 150 and 250 yards (one being 168 yards); the par 4 holes are between 250 and 450 yards; and the par 5 holes are between 475 and 600 yards (one being 476 yards).

What are the lengths of holes numbers 2, 6 and 7 respectively?

32
Peace Talks

The peace talks are ending, and round the circular table remain an equal number of delegates from each of the four parties. As principals, the Ultrasuttel (U) delegates sit together; likewise the Norveasters (N). As 'unrecognizables', no two delegates of either of their respective allies, the Souvesters (S) or the Vericutes (V), may do so.

Impasse is reached over selecting a Drafting Committee of four. Finally the senior U delegate proposes that selection be left to chance by counting clockwise, starting with the delegate on his left, and selecting every fifth man (narrowing the circle as each is picked out) until four are so chosen.

N and V hastily confer. The Vericutes have spotted that the Committee would become a U S monopoly; so N counter-propose that (starting from the same man) every ninth man should be picked out instead.

U look for the catch, and find it – an N V monopoly!

How many delegates sit round the table and in what order?

33

Light on the Matches

Six football sides, A, B, C, D, E and F, are all to play each other once with 2 points for a win, 1 point for a draw.

After some of the matches have been played a battered piece of paper is discovered on which have obviously been written particulars of the results so far.

All that can be read is shown below:

	Played	Won	Lost	Drawn	Goals	Goals	Points
A	2	1			4	2	
B	4				1	4	3
C			1			7	7
D	3				1	5	3
E						7	
F	5				2		7

Find who played whom and the score in each match.

51

34

Commuters and Crosswords

Eight of us – four father-and-son pairs – use the same compartment of the train going to work every day. The compartment holds ten, but it never arrives empty: Miller is always in the far left-hand corner with his back to the engine, and his son is often opposite him. We always enter in the same order, and each man sits down in turn as far from the door as possible; if he has a choice he consults his own wishes only. The four crossword puzzlers insist on sitting beside non-puzzlers; but Brown always sits beside Smith, who is a puzzler, and Bernard, another puzzler, sits beside his uncle whenever he has a choice. Jones always insists on facing the engine. Every father naturally enters before his son, but John is the only son to follow immediately after his father.

On Thursday everything went wrong. Young Miller was in his usual place, but his father was not there. John spent too long talking to Mary and scrambled in last. Consequently two puzzlers sat side by side, Brown sat opposite Smith, and Jones sat with his back to the engine.

My son, Sam, works in the same office as Robert. No son has the same initial for his Christian and surname. Robinson is bald.

Who am I, and what is my place in the queue?

35

Nuns

Recently I travelled on a 22-seater aircraft with a very mixed bunch of passengers. By birth, there were Americans, Italians, Greeks, Swedes, Germans and British. There was an equal number of each nationality and the sexes were equally represented. At least one of each nationality was married.

All except four of our company were married couples travelling together; but only in two cases were all of the same nationality married people. In only one case were the husband and wife of the same origin, and the national pairings were not duplicated.

I am British and married to the sister of the Swedish film star (recently divorced) travelling with us; both my lady compatriots are also married to Europeans. The party included a German bishop and two nuns. Of the Italians only two were married, the Contessa to a Swede and her only brother to an American. One of the Americans had an unmarried brother-in-law in the party.

What nationality are the nuns?

36

Inter-School Trophy

Annually in the Easter and summer terms from 1967 to 1971 Lanchester and Marbury competed in five matches at different sports. Points were given for a win (6 each for cricket and football, 4 each for hockey, swimming and athletics), the points being shared equally in the case of a draw or tie. The total points-score decided the annual winner of the Topp cup.

During this five-year period Lanchester won the cup three times, and Marbury won it twice, but their grand totals of points were equal. The winning margin decreased each year, from 12 points in 1967 to 2 points in 1971.

In each sport there was *one* draw or tie, the hockey being drawn in 1969. Marbury last won the cricket in 1968, a year in which they won the cup. Lanchester never won the swimming, but had the better record at athletics (which they won in 1967).

Deduce the results of all the matches in the series.

37

Fallen Leaves

Three leaves fall from a book. The total of the page numbers remaining in the second half of the book is now three times the total of the page numbers remaining in the first half.

The total of the page numbers on the fallen leaves lies between 1050 and 1070, and is the highest fall-out which could have produced this effect.

How many numbered pages did the book contain originally?

38

Sharing Sweets

The Binks family had a birthday party recently for Ann, the youngest child. A tin of toffees was shared among the seven youngest members of the family whose ages were all different and less than twenty. It was decided that the younger children should have more than the older; so Mr Binks suggested that each should receive the number obtained by dividing the total number of toffees by his or her age. This was done, and it so happened that all the divisions worked out exactly and no toffees were left over.

Mary received eighteen sweets.

How much older was she than Ann?

39

Bell's Weights

'Now,' says Bell at the pub, 'look intelligent and imaginative even if you don't look beautiful by any means.' We swallow the insult and look solemn. Bell likes his jokes and we like his puzzles.

'Imagine you have some scales, but only three weights. However, you have a heap of Grade A sand and a couple of bags; so you make two extra weights, one as heavy as all the first three put together, and the other twice as heavy as all the first three. Whereupon all the remaining sand is removed to a great distance.

'With these five weights you must be able to weigh 1 ounce, 2 ounces, 3, 4, and so on, as far as possible. No gaps in that lot. It's how far you can go to the first gap I'm after. Usual prize – one pint for the best score before closing time.'

What should Bell's five weights be to give the highest possible score?

40

Logical Will

Uncle George occasionally wasted time on Brain Teasers, and it was expected that his will would take an awkward form. But his five nephews were surprised to learn, after his death, that he had dictated his will to a solicitor who had no use for punctuation. The will ran as follows:

maurice is not to sing at my funeral service if stephen receives the envelope containing three thousand pounds alec is to have five thousand pounds if thomas receives less than maurice alec is to have twice what nigel has if thomas does not receive the envelope containing a thousand pounds stephen is to have exactly four thousand pounds

The nephews were confident that Uncle George always uttered complete sentences none of which contained more than one conditional clause. They also felt sure that what he had said to the solicitor allowed one way, and one way only, of distributing the five envelopes (containing £5000, £4000, £3000, £2000 and £1000) which Uncle George had left for them.

Who receives each envelope? And may Maurice sing at the funeral service?

41

Betting Prices

In the third race, the bookmakers' prices varied considerably and, in some cases, were unusual. At one time or another up to the start of the race, the odds quoted against one or more of the nine horses were: 2 to 1; 3 to 1; 4 to 1 . . . and all other whole numbers to 1 up to and including 28 to 1 (i.e. 27 different prices in all).

Just before the 'off' the Baron saw his chance. The prices then being offered by different bookmakers were such that, by staking a total of less than £100, and placing a whole number of £ on every one of the runners, he could ensure that, no matter which horse won, he would make an overall profit of exactly £13.

One horse was clear favourite. The other eight were 'paired' in the betting (i.e. there were four pairs, both horses in each pair being at the same price – the four prices all being different).

How much did the Baron stake in all, and at what five prices?

42

Jacob's Ladder

Joseph's garage, built at ground level on the side wall of his house, had uniform external dimensions of (exactly) 10 feet high by 10 feet wide. Wishing to paint from the outside a top-floor window frame over the garage, he positioned his longest ladder (whose length was over 30 feet) with its foot on the ground at such a distance from the garage that its top rested against the house wall at the maximum height possible. Discovering, however, that despite this he could not reach up to the window, he borrowed his neighbour Jacob's ladder and, positioning it similarly, found that he could now reach comfortably.

With each ladder, the length, distance and height referred to were all integral numbers of inches.

How much longer was Jacob's ladder than Joseph's, and how much higher on the wall did it reach?

43

Some Sticky Impedimenta

Uncle Bungle's carelessness and untidiness get more exasperating every day. He has always been very interested in football and I thought I could rely on him to let me know the situation in a set of matches in which five local teams (A, B, C, D and E) were each to play each other once.

All he was prepared to do, however, was to give me a messy piece of paper on which red ink had been fighting a losing battle against the assorted and mainly sticky impedimenta which my uncle kept in his pocket. I copied out what I could decipher – as follows:

	Played	Won	Lost	Drawn	Goals for	Goals against	Points
A	3				2	4	3
B	3					0	
C				0	1	1	
D	4			0		0	
E			2		1		1

I had just finished the copying when I heard the voice of my uncle in my ear.

'You really ought to be more careful,' he said. 'You've got one of those figures wrong.'

Which is the incorrect figure, and what was the score in each match?

44

Family Birthdays

I wrote to an American friend on 3 February 1964 and told him of the coincidence of our family birthdays. My wife and I, our three sons, and our four grandsons all have our birthdays on the same day of the week every year, though all our birthdays are different. When I wrote, I used the usual English form of the date – 3.2.64 – and I gave all our birthdays in that form also.

My third son received a cable from my friend on his birthday in 1964, but later I was surprised to get a cable from him myself on my eldest son's birthday. Next my eldest grandson received a cable on his right birthday, and I realized that we were all going to receive cables, but that my friend was, quite reasonably, reading my dates in the American form, i.e. he assumed that the letter had been sent on 2 March 1964.

However, I did not write to put him right, and my wife was the next person to get a cable; this was not on her birthday.

What was the day and date of her birthday in 1964?

45

Triangular Bridge

Three tables of bridge – A, B and C – are arranged in the form of a triangle. At each table the North and South seats are numbered 1 and 3 respectively and the East and West seats 2 and 4. The players who begin in these seats are described as A1, A2, A3, A4, B1 . . . and so on.

After each rubber certain players change their seats. The local rule is: of the winning pair the higher-numbered player moves to the highest-numbered vacant seat at the next table clockwise (that is, A to B, B to C, and C to A); of the losing pair the player in the lower-numbered seat moves to the next table counter-clockwise.

Last Saturday it happened that at each table the North/South pair won each alternate rubber. For the eighth rubber of the evening A1 played the North hand at Table C.

Who won the following rubber at table B?

46

Catering Crisis

The caterer at our Village Hall is in a quandary, for the Hall has been double-booked for next Saturday evening – by the Cricket Club and by the Darts Club.

Unfortunately the matter cannot be resolved until the return of the Vicar on Saturday morning. He is quite unpredictable in such decisions, and the caterer must order the food by Friday.

The Cricketers want 100 sausage rolls and 60 meat pies; the Darts Club wants 50 sausage rolls and 90 meat pies.

The caterer is empowered to spend exactly £6·00. He buys sausage rolls at 3p and sells at 4p; meat pies cost him 5p and sell at 8p. Any left-overs are disposed of at a loss to a local prep school, which pays 2p per sausage roll and 3p per pie.

What should the caterer order so as to make the best safe *profit no matter which club gets the booking? And what will that profit be?*

47

Silver Collection

Seven South Sea Island brothers found on the beach a broken box and mixed silver coins scattered. These were old British coins (sixpence, shilling, florin, half-crown and crown). 135 of them bore a man's head and fifty-four a woman's. The two younger brothers claimed the latter and their elders shared the former.

Being ignorant of the value of the coins they agreed to take twenty-seven each. First they laid the coins in heaps of each size. The senior brother then took seven coins from each of two heaps and smaller numbers from the other three heaps to make up twenty-seven coins. Each other brother then took the same numbers but each from a different order of heaps.

Unknown to themselves, the five elders had equal money value. The boys also had equal value, but greater than their elders.

What were the values in old British currency?

Note: Respective values 6d., 12d., 24d., 30d., 60d.

48

Dancing Partners

Five men and their wives made up a party to go to a ball. Each man was a brother of one of the ladies and each lady a sister of one of the men, but no two men had married each other's sisters.

In one of the dances they paired off so that no man danced with his wife or his sister.

Mr Quayle danced with Jane and was the only man to dance with his sister's husband's sister.

Gladys danced with her husband's sister's husband, Mr Tern.

Mr Swan danced with Mr Pigeon's sister, Florence.

Mr Robin danced with Harriet.

The fifth lady's name was Ida.

What was her surname?

49

Hare Hill

Says Bell to us at the pub, 'You might like to exercise your brains a bit, unless they're fuddled with weak beer.

'George sets off in the car from here for Hare Hill top at two minutes past two and stops half an hour for tea at the Hatters, which is supposed to be at half-way but it's 2½ kilometres farther on. His wife takes over the driving until they arrive back at the Hatters, and George drives the rest of the way home. Same route in both directions. He spends twenty minutes at the top of the hill; it takes him five minutes to park the car and he's in the house at 6.37. What time did he get to Hare Hill? Speeds? George does 30 kilometres an hour uphill, 42 downhill and 35 on the flat. His wife's statistics are 30, 45, 36. No vulgarity if you please.

'Yes, there could be a few ups and downs. Well, on the way out neither driver does more down than up. No, I only said there could be ups and downs. No guarantees. How high is a hill? Well it's a hill, isn't it?

'You think I've missed something out? Well, I haven't, but I'll tell you something for nothing. On the way back neither driver does more up than down and a kilometre's 1,100 yards. I'll be generous; if anybody gets an answer that can't be more than 10 minutes out I'll award the usual pint.'

What time of arrival at Hare Hill top wins the prize?

50

Logicians in Conference

At the International Conference of Logicians, the delegates were given odd numbers running from 1 to 999; to increase their enjoyment, they did not wear these but spent their time deducing each other's numbers.

I knew nobody's number, not even my own; but the secretary of the conference, who knew everyone's number, told me that the four Irish delegates had consecutive odd numbers; he introduced them to me by name, beginning with the man who had the lowest number and working his way up to the man with the highest.

As I met each, I said (by way of suitable conversation), 'Do you have a number which is either a perfect square or a perfect cube or both?' Each of the four replied 'Yes' or 'No'; I then turned to the secretary and said, 'I know that I have not been given four truthful replies.'

'That's true,' he replied. 'But if I now tell you whether one, two, three or four Irishmen lied to you, you will know for certain what numbers these delegates hold.' The secretary is a truthful man.

What then was the conference number of the Irishman whom I met first?

51

Golf Scores

Tom, Gerry and John playing golf scored by points.

At each hole six points were awarded. Where all took the same number of strokes, all scored two points; where two took the same and the third took more, each of the two scored three points; where one took fewer than either of the others he scored four points and, if the others took the same number of strokes, each scored one point – if not, both points went to the one with the lower score for the hole.

Over the eighteen holes played, John scored 19 points. At exactly five holes he scored nothing. Tom alone won points at every hole, and finished one point ahead of Gerry.

The number of holes at which two players each took more strokes than the third was less than 9.

At how many holes did Gerry score exactly (a) 1 point; (b) 2 points; (c) 3 points; (d) 4 points ?

52

Equal Marks

Tom, Dick and Harry took a test in each of five subjects. Each test was marked out of a total of 40. In grand total each boy obtained half-marks, and no boy scored the same mark in two or more tests. Each boy's best and third-best marking totalled one fifth more than the total of his best and fourth-best, and each boy's worst mark exceeded 10. The aggregate of the three boys' marks in each of four subjects was the same, the highest single mark going to Tom. The second highest was scored by Dick in the remaining subject.

How many marks did Harry get in that one?

53

The Un-Flats

On the Island of Imperfection very little is as it should be and even the Flats aren't – hence they are called the Un-Flats.

There are three tribes on the Island – the Pukkas, who always tell the truth; the Wotta-Woppas, who never tell the truth; and the Shilli-Shallas who make statements which are alternately true and false, or false and true. We are concerned with three inhabitants of the Island, one from each tribe, who each live in one of the 30 Un-Flats. Numbers 11–20 are reserved for the Shilli-Shallas, numbers 1–10 for one of the other two tribes, and numbers 21–30 for the third tribe.

The three with whom this story deals are called Askew, Bent and Crooked, in no particular order. They each make two statements (in accordance, of course, with their tribal characteristics) as follows:

ASKEW: 1. The number of my flat is a multiple of 4.
         2. Bent lives at flat number 7.
BENT: 1. Askew's number is a multiple of 12.
         2. The Shilli-Shalla's number is not a multiple of 6.
CROOKED: 1. I live at flat 18.
         2. The number of Askew's flat is even.

Find to which tribe each of the three belongs and the number of his flat.

54

Prime Flats

The number of families living on one floor in a block of flats is prime. Each family consists of a pair of parents and at least one child; the number of people in each family and the total number of people in all families are prime numbers. Everyone has recently had a birthday anniversary, and each person's age is a prime number. No one is older than 40, and every parent was at least 23 before his first child was born. Each of the prime numbers described above occurs exactly twice.

The sum of the ages of each family is a prime number, and a different one in each case. The sum of the ages of everyone is a prime number.

What are the ages of the people in each family?

Note: In this problem the number 1 is counted as a prime number.

55

Stars

There was a small party in the officers' mess and Jeremy, as usual, was showing off. He thinks he is a wizard at mental arithmetic. After solemnly counting heads he said that the total of the stars worn by the captains was two more than the total officers he could see. Moreover, the said captains' stars were ten more than the second-lieutenants' and twenty fewer than those of the lieutenants. (Loud cheers from the lieutenants.)

Actually, we all laughed. Jeremy could not see one of us who was bending down behind the bar. When old Waffles popped up he promptly went one better than Jeremy, pointing out that our total party was a prime number and the total of each rank was prime. Quick thinking, what?

I suppose everyone knows that a captain wears three stars on each shoulder, lieutenants two stars, and a second-lieutenant only one. It was lucky that there were no more senior officers present, for it turned out to be quite a party.

How many full lieutenants were there?

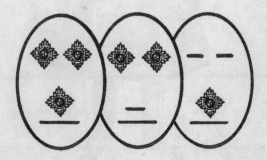

56

What's My Age?

I recently had an odd letter from a puzzle addict, who wrote: 'I know that you are between 25 and 80, and I've made a bet (at fair odds) that I can deduce your age from your Yes/No answers to the following questions: 1. Are you under 55? 2. Is your age a prime number? 3. If the digits of your age are reversed, is the result a prime number? 4. Is the digital root of your age *even*? Please reply on enclosed stamped addressed postcard.'

I did so and had his reply a few days later: 'Many thanks. As soon as I read your first three answers I knew that the fourth answer must lead me to your age. You are . . .' (and he gave a figure wrong by well over 20 years).

Puzzled, I rechecked my four answers and found to my horror that I had carelessly transposed two of them and so had misled him.

How old am I?

Note: The digital root of a number is found by adding its digits, continuing the process if necessary until a single digit remains; e.g. $23 \rightarrow 2+3 = 5$; $78 \rightarrow 7+8 = 15 \rightarrow 1+5 = 6$.

57

Ali's Counter Move

Ali and Baba are playing the Chay game. Ali has a bag containing 12 numbered tickets, 3 each of numbers 1, 2, 3, 4 (all numbers represented by strokes). Baba has 6 double-sided counters containing the same twelve numbers, and a board of six squares.

Ali draws 6 tickets from his bag one at a time, calling out the number as he does so. At each call Baba selects a counter with that number on one of its sides and places it face up in a square. If in 6 calls he fills 6 squares, he wins. Once a counter is laid it stays. The counter-couplings are so arranged that 5 squares could always be filled if the numbers were known beforehand.

But, unnoticed by Baba, Ali has slyly added 1 stroke each to 2 of his opponent's counters. As a result, Baba frequently places no more than 3 or 4 counters, and at last comes a deal when, after Ali has called 'Two', 'One', he calls a third number and Baba cannot fill it.

It is the last straw.

Baba, having lost many pice and much temper, angrily examines the four remaining counters. Three of them are identical couplings!

'Ah! wicked one,' he cries, 'you have forged my counters!' And, throwing them down, he clears for action.

What couplings are on these 4 counters?

58

100-yard Race

Harry, Kenneth, Lionel, Martin, Nicholas and Oliver were the competitors in the 100-yard race on Sports Day. They wore cards numbered 1, 2, 3, 4, 5, 6 but not in that order. In no case was the position of any of the competitors the same as his card-number but two of the competitors had positions equal to each other's card-number.

Nicholas was fifth and his card-number was the same as Kenneth's position. Harry's card-number was the same as Oliver's position, which was fourth. Martin's card-number was 1.

It was found that the sum of the products of each competitor's position and card-number was 61.

Place the competitors in the order in which they finished the race and give their card-numbers.

59

Grand Vizier

Sever-Nek the Grand Vizier was suspicious of the influence which Azi-Muth, the Sultan's wily tutor, was gaining over his young pupil, and had determined to have him removed when chance played into his hands.

The Sultan had a collection of nearly 2000 small square tiles, all the same size in various colours, and one day to please his tutor had arranged some of them into a square with a pretty central design and a border. Then he announced that he had made two smaller equal squares using the same pieces. 'But that is impossible,' said Azi-Muth, 'there must be some left over.'

There was one over, and Sever-Nek, happening to pass by, put his foot over it. 'Surely not,' he said. 'His Serene Highness has made a most interesting discovery. No doubt the same thing can be done again. Let us add some extra tiles from the box to those already used.' Nothing loath the Sultan soon produced a larger square from which he almost made two smaller identical squares. This time he was one tile short.

'Your Serene Highness must have dropped this one on the floor,' said the Grand Vizier, moving his foot. 'Allow me to complete the design.' The discomfiture of the outwitted tutor was no less complete than his disgrace.

How many extra tiles were taken from the box to make the larger square?

60

Lifts

I forget which floor of the tower Black works on, but I know that he is four floors above Green, and that White is one floor below the top floor of the tower. I have also noticed that there are two lifts which move at constant speeds to the top and bottom of the tower, with five-second halts at each floor; and one can change lifts every time they meet (moving in opposite directions) or pass (moving in the same direction).

Each morning, when the tower opens, one lift leaves the top as the other leaves the bottom; their first meeting is at Black's floor, their third at Green's floor, their sixth at White's floor – and, soon afterwards, they pass for the first time.

How many floors are there in the tower above Black's floor?

61

Gold Cup

Although 42 horses (numbered 1 to 42) were originally entered for the Teaser Gold Cup, only 38 took part in the race.

The number of the horse which came second in the race exceeded the number of the winner by the same number as that by which the number of the third horse exceeded the number of the second.

When the numbers of the four non-runners were placed in numerical order, the difference between each number and the next was the same in every case, and that difference was the same as the difference between the number of the winner and the number of the second.

The sum of the highest and lowest numbers of the four non-runners was equal to the sum of the numbers of the horses which came first, second and third.

One of the first three horses was numbered 15. Horses numbered 24 and 28 fell at the third fence, and were not remounted.

What were the numbers of the four non-runners?

62

Tennis Party

Frankie, Sandy and Pat arranged a lawn tennis party with Carol, Evelyn and Hilary. All three boys played one another in a set each of singles; the girls did likewise. Sandy and Hilary each won both their sets; Pat and Carol each lost both of theirs. None went to more than ten games.

All then played in two out of three sets of mixed doubles, with no boy partnering the same girl twice. Pat, partnered by Hilary, beat Frankie and Carol 6–3 but later, with Carol as partner, won only four games. The score in the remaining set was 6–0. In the end, each girl had won the same number of games altogether.

(*a*) *How many games did Frankie win playing against Sandy ?*
(*b*) *Which players won respectively 16 and 17 games altogether ?*

63 ✓

The Lie Drug

The doctor in our little village has for a long time been experimenting with lie drugs, and one afternoon he was trying out his latest concoction on the secretary of one of the three local football teams (A, B, and C).

The secretary had just been given a powerful dose, and seemed to be in rather a coma as he sat trying, at the doctor's request, to fill in details of the numbers of matches played, won, lost, etc. (The three teams are all to play each other once.)

Suddenly the doctor snatched the piece of paper from him with a cry of delight. 'Success!' he said. 'Every single figure here is incorrect.'

I looked at the document and it read as follows:

	Played	Won	Lost	Drawn	Goals for	Goals against	Points
A		0					2
B	1			0	1		
C		1		1	0	1	0

(2 points for a win, 1 for a draw)

I found it interesting that – perhaps because of a subconscious desire for truth in spite of the drug – although all the figures given were incorrect it was possible, knowing this, to discover details of all the matches played.

Find who played whom and the score in each match. (Not more than 3 goals were scored in any match.)

64

Splat

The game of Splat was invented by the children to use up the remaining cards from a bezique pack: 2 to 6 inclusive of the four suits. When all the cards are dealt, each player has the same number of cards. The players then add the score in their hands, counting 4 for each spade pip, 3 for each heart, 2 for each diamond and 1 for each club. The cards are then played in tricks without following suit, the winner of each trick being the player of the card with the largest score based on 1 for each spade pip, 2 for each heart, 3 for each diamond and 4 for each club. The dealer leads to the first trick; thereafter the winner of the last trick. Play is not subtle: each player plays his highest valued card, if this is higher than each card played so far in a trick; otherwise he plays his lowest card. When all the tricks are played, each player adds the points from the cards in the tricks which he has taken – based on the scoring system for the play of the cards – to the score from his hand, the winner being the player with the highest total.

In a game recently John got half of the points in his hand from one card, and Andrew, the winner, scored 1 more point in the first trick than the total score of the player who came second. No player had two cards with the same number of pips or two cards of the same suit in his hand, but all except John had two cards (and only two) with the same score.

What was the last card played in the game?

65

Regatta

For our last regatta the sailing club decided that a motor-boat race of six laps over a five-mile course on our lake would be a popular attraction. We have four old tubs mostly used for fishing; each has a different speed (in whole miles an hour) between 9 and 29 m.p.h. The secretary had the idea of a trial run up and down the course the week before the race to establish reasonable time allowances.

The four boats each ran the trial in still water in a whole number of minutes, and their time differences were tripled to give their starting times for the actual race. The fastest boat would cross the starting line at noon precisely, the others preceding it by their allotted number of minutes to give, in theory, a dead-heat at the finish.

Unfortunately, owing to heavy rains in the hills, for the next week a current ran through the lake straight down the course at 5 m.p.h. (The secretary wrongly called it 5 knots, but he is a sailing man.) The race started as planned, but against the unexpected current (and in the pouring rain) the slowest boat dropped out. After a hurried meeting in the flooded club-house the committee decided to reduce the course to five laps, so that the race could finish before lunch.

The three fastest boats finished the shortened course, surprisingly maintaining their top speeds, in an exact number of minutes.

How many minutes separated the winner and third boats at the finish?

66

Finger Trouble

The Wabu tribesmen, though invariably truthful, are inveterate thieves, and this despite a tribal law which requires any man convicted of theft to have one finger amputated. Few of them now have a full complement and, since they count on their fingers, their answers to numerical questions are confusing to the outsider. (For instance, an 8-fingered man gives his answers to base 8, so that our 100 is for him 144.)

Despite these handicaps they are keen cricketers, and I recently watched their First Eleven. The Chief told me: 'Only little Dojo has 10 fingers; the worst-equipped are Abo, Bunto and Coco with 4 apiece.' (I need hardly add that the Wabu would never elect a Chief who had been *convicted* of theft.)

Later I asked some members of the team how many fingers – thumbs of course included – the Eleven totalled. Epo said: '242', and Foto agreed. Gobo said: '132', and Hingo agreed. Kinko added: 'I have more fingers than Iffo.'

How many fingers each have Epo, Hingo, Iffo, and Jabo (the wicket-keeper)?

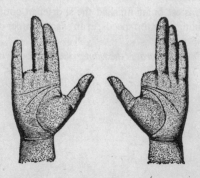

67

Here Comes the Bride

The hall has an oak-beamed ceiling, is 32 feet wide and 24 feet high. During redecorating, a stage 5 feet wide strewn with painters' equipment fills the lower half of the short south wall. Wet paint largely covers the upper half of each of the off-stage long walls.

In the top south-east corner, slim Ara, running speed 14 inches per second, dropping speed 12 feet per second; in the top south-west corner, her old rival, plump Chne, running speed 11 inches per second. She never risks dropping. Both have a run limit of 100 feet. Both are geometers. Both are lovesick for Bud.

Bud, from his den at the bottom middle of the north wall, would a-wooing go. He would walk at his usual rate of exact inches per second along the centre line of the floor to the staging in exact seconds. Ara had anticipated, 'It will be too far for him. He will tire and return. I shall meet him at his den.' Chne felt, 'He won't get far. If he doesn't tire too soon I shall meet him as and when our paths join.'

All started at once, Ara and Chne each taking her planned route, this for each being in whole feet.

Exact seconds later Bud tired. 'Nothing wooing,' he sighed. So he waited. And from either side the lovers closed in . . .

Wedded! By an inch!

How long did his bride keep Bud waiting?

68

Birthdays

Five men were talking about their birthdays at the club last night.
They wrote down their birth-dates in the usual form, e.g. 29.8.43.

Arthur, the oldest, noticed that no two of the fifteen numbers
were the same.

Bill, the youngest, observed that if each man multiplied together
the three numbers representing his own birth-date, the five answers
would all be the same.

Charlie, who was nearly a year younger than David, pointed out
that each year-number was greater than all the day-numbers and
each day-number greater than all the month-numbers.

No one was born in January and no one was born in or after
1936.

What was Ernest's birth-date?

69

Ribbon Counter

'Puzzle here,' says Bell at the pub. 'Chap has a ribbon shop, sells the stuff by the inch, no commercial sense. He's barmy anyway; look how he measures it. His counter is exactly 100 inches long and he's marked it off into 16 bits, 6 of 11 inches, 2 of 6 inches, 3 of 5 inches, 1 of 3 inches and 4 of 1 inch, and he can measure any number of inches up to a hundred, that is, by picking the right pair of marks.

'You have to sort the spaces out; but I'll tell you, all the 11 inches are together round about the middle – well, a bit to the right, but not as much as 4 inches off centre. You get the idea? For most measurements he's using a kind of feet and inches with eleven inches to the foot.

'Young Green is nearly right: he can't measure 99 inches unless there's a 1-inch space at one end, but he doesn't need a 1-inch at the other end for 98 inches; he does it with 2 1-inch spaces at the same end; but there might be a 1-inch at the other end, all the same, and there might not.

'In answer to two foolish questions, the ribbon must be measured single thickness, no folding; and it's a straight counter, it's not circular.

'Usual prize, one pint.'

How were the spaces arranged from left to right?

70

Delphic Oracle

Delphi has three computers, in order to confuse the faithful. The 1969 one always gives a true answer; the 1960 one always gives an untrue answer; the 1965 one is quite unpredictable.

Professor Binary, who is visiting the shrine, fed to each computer in turn the question 'What is the date of the largest computer?' The first computer replied, '1969'; the second replied, 'Not 1960'; and Binary, who could see the size though not the date of the computers as they replied, had no need to study the third computer's reply since he now knew the answer to his question.

What is the date of the largest computer?

71

Air Ways

Al, Bill, Cab, Don, Ed, Fred, Gil, Hal, and Ian were waiting at the airport. Three would take a plane going east, three a plane going north, and three a plane going south.

Hal, but neither Ian nor Fred, was going south. Al would be travelling with Don or Cab; Fred would be travelling with Bill or Ed.

Gil, unlike Ian, would be travelling east. Cab would take a seat next to Ed or Al. Ian would travel in a different plane from Bill, and in a different plane from Cab.

If Don would still be waiting at the airport after Bill and Ed had left, who were the three going north?

72

Internationals

Some years ago in the International Football Championship, with the four countries playing each other once, and 2 points being earned for a win and 1 for a draw, England ended up with 5 points against Scotland's 3 points although the latter had scored just as many goals in the Championship as the other three countries put together.

In the concluding match, in which Ireland was at home to Scotland, the former had hoped to treble their points score, but instead they lost 1–3.

What was the score in the England v. Ireland match?

73

Dothemens Hall

Miss Machiavel takes the sixth form for logic at Dothemens Hall, a very modern school for girls. She has always maintained that in order to make friends and influence men a girl must see clearly the vital distinction between what is true and what is false. 'If you want warm fingers and a cosy home,' she has said, 'you must be prepared to play with the fire of deception.' And – another homely adage – 'if a lie is worth telling it is worth telling thoroughly'.

After they had heard the results of their Advanced Level papers in Logic, therefore, Miss Machiavel got four of her pupils, Priscilla, Queeny, Rachel and Susan, to make various remarks, which should all be false, about their grades. (There are seven possibilities: a candidate may get grade A, B, C, D or E, at the Advanced Level, or she may get an Ordinary Level grade (O) or she may fail (F). The possibilities, therefore, in order of merit are A, B, C, D, E, O and F.)

The remarks made were as follows:

PRISCILLA: 1. No one had a grade higher than B.
           2. Queeny's grade was lower than B.

QUEENY: 1. My grade was A.
           2. Priscilla got one of the three highest grades.

RACHEL: 1. My grade was higher than D.
           2. Susan's grade was higher than Priscilla's.

SUSAN: 1. My grade was lower than E.
           2. Queeny's grade was higher than Rachel's.

Unfortunately their logic training had not been completely successful, and one of these eight remarks was true, though the other seven were false.

Which one was true? Find each girl's grade. (Their grades were all different.)

74

Catastrophe

It happened on 23 September in the hours of daylight just beneath the village clock, which was working and striking the quarter hours correctly all day. There were five eye-witnesses. I asked them all when it happened. Each gave four answers, two of which were true and two were lies.

Alf said, 'It was before noon. The minute hand of the clock was in the bottom half of the dial. It was more than three hours from noon. The clock had struck a quarter to in the last five minutes.'

Bert said, 'It was before noon. The minute hand of the clock was in the top half of the dial. It was more than three hours from noon. The hands of the clock were at right angles to each other.'

Charlie said, 'It was after noon. The minute hand of the clock was in the bottom half of the dial. The clock had struck a quarter to in the last five minutes. The hands of the clock were coincident.'

Don said, 'The minute hand of the clock was in the top half of the dial. It was less than three hours from noon. The clock had struck half past in the last five minutes. The hands of the clock were opposite each other.'

Edward said, 'It was after noon. It was less than three hours from noon. The clock had struck a quarter past in the last five minutes. The hands of the clock were coincident.'

When did it happen (to the nearest minute)?

Note: There is no catch about daylight saving, the equation of time or mathematical limits. Daylight lasted from 6 a.m. to 6 p.m.; noon was at 12; the changeover from a.m. to p.m. was instantaneous.

75

Index Cabinet

My index cabinet has twelve rows of drawers, three in each row. It is arranged alphabetically with every letter starting with a new drawer – except for X and Z for which there is no space.

Each drawer can hold 24 cards; but each initial has a different number of cards, with only one drawer having fewer than 13 cards.

I shall soon have to buy another cabinet, for all the middle drawers are already completely full. But luckily at present half the initials have under the average number of cards – which of course is only held by one initial.

What is the highest number of cards the third column of drawers can still receive?

76

Gouttes d'Or

The conical glasses at the Hôtel d'Or hold one eighth of a litre and are embellished from base to brim with a picture of Bacchus. In making the hotel's famous Gouttes d'Or, sold at NF 5·20, it was customary to fill the glass up to Bacchus's neck (four fifths of the way up the glass) and then to add an olive; the profit on raw materials was a modest 100 per cent.

Gaston, the barman, has decided that he must make the more realistic profit of 400 per cent. So now the olive is put in first and then liquor is added up to the level of Bacchus's chest (three fifths of the way up the glass). The price has been reduced to NF 4·80.

Gaston explained: 'Ze olives are of standard size and cost me 1 centime a c.c. . . . Yes, I *could* put in ze olive after measuring out ze liquor – but zen it would be necessary to charge . . .'

To charge how much?

77

The Sheep Pen

Every spring Tom fences a rectangular acre pen in his top field. The long north side along the road, being well hedged, needs no fence. Tom always starts at the north-west corner and finishes at the north-east corner adjoining the Red Cow.

This year, he went to the barn where he has a stock of fence pieces from 4 feet long upwards, loaded up the 57 pieces of 4 different foot-lengths that he knew were required, drove off, and dropped pieces on the way.

Setting to work, he completed the west and south fences each with an exact number of 'bigguns'. After fixing one 'biggun' to the east fence he discovered that a piece of the second longest size was missing. 'I knows I loaded one of 'em,' he said, and then, examining the remaining heap, 'Half of them's bigguns; so bigguns is all here, but the others is five short and I bean't goin' back.'

So he dismantled and rebuilt a shorter south fence, and then with exactly enough, built a fence straight to the Red Cow.

With what?

78

Telephone Number

Fred was an exasperating person; he would never give a straight answer to a straight question. The other day I was seeing him off at a bus stop and he said, just as the bus was coming, 'Give me a ring some time.'

'I will,' I said, and asked him for his telephone number.

'It has five digits,' he replied, 'and the first two are the same as my wife's age while the last two are my age.'

'But I don't know how old you are,' I said, 'except that you are less than 70.'

'There's no need to be rude,' he said, 'I am older than my wife by as many years as our son's age.'

'What has he got to do with your telephone number?' I asked.

'Oh!' he replied, 'his age is the middle digit.'

'That doesn't help much,' I said.

'It's divisible by 259,' he shouted, as the bus whisked him away.

'That's a *great* help,' I shouted back, and it really was.

What was Fred's telephone number?

79

Pints All Round

'Little puzzle here,' says Bell at the pub squeezing himself in.
'Move up. Now, we are seven sat round the table. I am No. 1,
naturally, and you are 2, 3 up to 7 and back to No. 1 clockwise.
These cards numbered 1 to 7 I shuffle and deal. If you have your
own number say "Hit!" Only one hit? Good! Pass the cards to
your left one place. Double hit? Bad. The trick is to find out how
the cards should be dealt for a single hit each time the cards are
passed. I'll make it easy. I always get the first hit and then numbers
2 and 6 get their hits as early as possible after that. Everything's
clockwise, numbering, dealing and passing.

'Usual prize, one pint.

'Difficult? It's a pushover. If you're thirsty I'll give you a pint.
Let's have a look at your cards. Anybody can see number 6 is going
to come up last. Swap them round a bit. Hold on! Now you've got
5 then 2 then 7 so when 5 gets a hit so does 7. You've got to avoid
that kind of thing.'

*In what order should the cards be dealt beginning with No. 1 clock-
wise?*

80

Death of a Bishop

Our local railway runs straight, beside a road, for 4½ miles through Wessex and then for 4½ miles through Barsetshire. It has a terminus at each end, of course, and eight other stations, equally spaced, between the termini. One train runs on the line each day, going to Barsetshire in the morning and back to Wessex in the afternoon.

Last Friday the train had only five passengers. Each one got in at a Wessex station, got out at a Barsetshire station, walked by the shortest route to another Barsetshire station, and took the afternoon train from there back to Wessex. Both in the morning and in the afternoon, one man joined or left the train at each station. Of the five men, Alec had the longest rail journey (14 miles) and Clym had the shortest; Diggory and Giles had the longest walks; and Jude never turned his back on Wessex. All the men travelled different distances by rail, but all did exactly half their rail journey in the morning and half in the afternoon.

Dr Proudie was murdered last Friday morning in the middle station of the five that are in Barsetshire. His murderer was the man who left the morning train at that station.

Who was the murderer? How far did he travel by train?

81

Birthday Party

The party consisted of three who were exactly six years of age, three who were exactly seven, and three who were exactly eight.

Although each one declined to give her age, none spoke anything but the truth. Susan said that she was younger than Sarah and that Lindy was older than Libby. Cathy told us that she was younger than Claire and that Lucy was younger than Sally. Libby disclosed that she, but not Cathy, was the same age as Susan; Katie agreed.

The initial letters of the names of the three six-year-olds were all different; so were those of the three seven-year-olds and those of the three eight-year-olds.

What were the names of those who were (a) six years old; (b) seven; (c) eight?

82

Grazing Rights

I own two square fields by my house, and the sides of each are exact numbers of yards. Although neither field is all that much over 10 acres, the difference between their areas, of exactly one acre, is not easily seen.

After some prolonged bargaining the previous autumn, I eventually told a farmer he could have the grazing rights on the larger field for the whole of 1972 for £61, which he duly paid me. However, when I returned home after spending the winter months abroad, I found that the farmer, not realizing which field was the larger, had been grazing his beasts on the smaller field instead.

I explained to him therefore that he had unwittingly been cheating himself and that, in order to restore the grazing fee per acre to no higher than the level I had in fact conceded, I would allow him to continue grazing the field, for the requisite whole number of days into 1973, without charge.

How many additional full days' grazing must I give him?

83

Emblems Are Out

On the Island of Imperfection there are three tribes – the Pukkas who always tell the truth, the Wotta Woppas who never tell the truth, and the Shilli-Shallas who make statements which are alternately true and false, or false and true.

In the old days it was easy to distinguish between these tribes for they all wore their tribal emblems. But things are very slack now, you can't tell a Wotta-Woppa from a Shilli-Shalla, and some of us are afraid that other essential standards may be on the way out. So far, however, whatever they may look like, they have not yet departed from their age-old tribal habits. But I'm afraid that I can give no information about the tribes of the three inhabitants of the Island with which this story is concerned.

These three all live in different houses, in the same road, which has houses numbered from 10 to 55 inclusive:

They speak as follows:

A: 1. A's number is greater than B's.
   2. My number is a multiple of 8.
   3. C's third remark is true.

B: 1. A is not a Wotta-Woppa.
   2. C's number is twice a prime.
   3. A makes the same number of true statements as I do.

C: 1. A is not a Shilli-Shalla.
   2. B's second remark is true.
   3. If C's number is reversed it has no prime factors other than 2.
   4. B's number is greater than C's.

Find the tribes to which A, B, and C belong and discover as much as you can about the numbers of their three houses.

84

Three Pairs of Twins

The logic master summoned his three brilliant pairs of twins, and said, 'To each of you I am giving two numbers. Multiply them together and note the product. All the numbers are two-digit prime numbers; all are different; the highest product is less than 1,000 and is exactly 50 more than the lowest product. Now, those of you who know more about the six products than some of the others hold up your hands.'

Albert, Betty and Charles raised their hands, but Donald, Ella and Fay did not.

Then he said, 'The sum of the Greens' products equals the sum of the Halls'. Now those of you who know less than the others hold up your hands.'

The Hall boys raised their hands, and the Ivers sniggered.

Then he said, 'What else would you like to know to resolve the whole problem?'

Albert and Ella both got up, and, pointing to each other, said, 'I should like to know how many of the digits in her (or his) product occur in mine.'

Before the master could say anything all six said, 'I know the lot now.'

Who had what products?

85

Badberg Clock

At the village of Badberg, hidden away in the Alps, there is a town clock of a certain antiquity whose maker was a wealthy but inexpert amateur. After the ornate instrument had been installed it was found that the hands stood still during the equal intervals between successive strokes of the hour on the massive bell. Naturally, the clock was always slow.

The placid villagers became accustomed to the erratic behaviour of their imposing timepiece. Only after the death of its donor did his nephew dare to tackle the problem. Finding it impossible to alter the incomprehensible striking mechanism, he modified the movement to run at a constant higher speed so that the hands showed the correct time at least when the clock struck certain hours.

Though the hands still stop for the same period between successive strokes of the bell, the villagers can now see and hear the correct time every six hours.

At what hours does the clock make its first stroke correctly?

Home Meadow

The triangular Home Meadow at Cowpleasure Farm is bounded on the west and south by straight fences running due north and due east from the farmhouse; its other fence forms one side of a square field known as Starvecrow. The south fence of Home Meadow is the shared north boundary of two contiguous square fields, Paddock and Rookery, whose total area is just half that of Starvecrow.

Farmer Nettle has just refenced the whole outer perimeter (i.e. excluding fences common to two or more fields). He used 146 equal sections of fencing, none of which needed bending or cutting.

He plans to replace the other fences next year using the same type of section.

How many such sections will he need?

Don't worry about gates; they are incorporated in some standard sections.

87

National Anthem

The National Anthem of Bahrein Teza exploits such brilliant technique that it is only performed by Bahreini musicians, and by them only on rare occasions such as the Coronation and Founding Festivals.

The work is a composition of 32 bars of Common Time.

The violin score contains equal numbers of minims, crotchets and quavers. Thirty of these are dotted notes, including equal numbers of dotted minims and crotchets.

Half of the undotted notes in the score are semiquavers.

How many notes do the fiddlers play?

88

Cross Country

Tom, Dick and Harry had come up the school together and in three successive years had competed in the Junior, Colts and Senior cross-country races.

Every year they finished in the same positions but interchanged so that no boy came in the same position twice. The same applied to the numbers on their vests, all six numbers being different, odd and greater than 1.

When each boy multiplied his position number by the number he was wearing at the time, the nine results were all different and together totalled 841.

Dick beat the other two in the Junior race but the number he was wearing was smaller than his position number; but he was wearing the highest card number in the Senior race and this was smaller than his position number.

Harry's three products had a sum smaller than that of either of the other two.

What were the three boys' positions in the Colts race and what numbers were they wearing?

89

British Triangles

British Triangles, naturally, stand on horizontal bases with their points upwards. All their sides, never more than a sensible 60 inches, and their heights measure an exact number of inches. No B.T. is isosceles or right-angled.

You can often put more than one B.T. on a common base. On a base of 28 inches 8 B.T.s are erected.

What are their heights?

90

Logic Club

Five members of the Logic Club sat in the bar and looked out of the window at their five cars. As each man knew only which car he himself owned, they decided on an exercise: each man would make two statements, one of which would be true and the other untrue, and the first man who was able to deduce with certainty the ownership of all the other four cars would stand up. It was agreed that each man could make his true statement either first or second, as he chose.

Anstey said: 'I do not own the Rover. I own the Singer.'

Briggs said: 'I do not own the Vauxhall. I do not own the Wolseley.'

Crane said: 'I can now tell for certain which car Anstey owns. I have never in my life owned a Triumph.'

Denby said: 'I own the Triumph. I do not own the Singer.'

Edwards said: 'I can now tell for certain which car belongs to Crane. I do not own the Singer.'

There was a pause after each man had spoken; but, though everyone made all possible deductions from these statements and gave everyone else credit for making all possible deductions too, nobody in fact stood up until Edwards had finished speaking.

Who stood up then ? And who owns the Rover ?

Cash Crossword

One day before the introduction of decimal currency I went shopping. First I visited the bank, where I bought a cheque for 2d. and then cashed it for a multiple of £10. I then visited a licensed betting shop and collected the money due to me from a bet made previously on an outsider to win. I then bought the goods described in the clues below. At no time had I more than £100 in my possession.

A	B	C	D
E		F	
	G		
H	I	J	
K			
L			

CLUES

Across

A. The date of the expedition.
E. The cost of the handkerchiefs.
F. The cost of the screws.
G. The odds on the horse.
H. My son's age at the time.
J. The number of shillings staked on the horse. This is a prime number.

K. The number of beads bought at 1d. a dozen. (see B down.)
L. The amount of money I had on leaving the bank. It is also the number of pennies which make up the sum I had at the start of the expedition.

Down

A. The amount of money I had at the end of the expedition.

B. The cost of the beads. (See K across.)

C. The cost of the waistcoat. This is not a prime number.

D. The date of my son's birth.

I. The amount of money I had at the start of the expedition.

J. The number of pennies spent on stamps. This is a prime number.

Note: Dates, sums of money, and the odds are given in the usual form but omitting any vertical strokes or other separating devices: e.g. 1211 could represent 1 February 1911, £1/2/11, £12/1/1 or 121 to 1, but *not* £12/11/0 or £12/0/11. It could also represent 12s. 11d.

92

Fairies in the Garden

A man of letters, well known to me, sees one day from his study window a number of those stone fairy things cluttering his back lawn. With a cry of rage he rushes into the garden intent on destroying these futile emblems of medieval superstition. Suddenly he stops.

He observes that the fairies have been ingeniously placed so that, now here, now there, in nineteen different directions they lie in straight lines with just three of them in a row. Much abashed he writes to me '. . . you couldn't possible get more than twenty lines. Send the design to the *Sunday Times*; they might give you a lot of money.'

There are 9 red fairies and 3 black ones and each red has more lines through it than any black one. The lawn is 60 foot square. There is a post at the middle of the house side and the 9 reds form a symmetrical pattern about a line up the garden from the post to the middle of the opposite side. One red is 15 feet up this line, another is 12 feet up and 6 feet right, a third is 20 feet up 10 feet left, and a fourth is 60 feet up 30 feet right which is in the corner. You have to place the three blacks and the remaining 5 reds. It looks very nice too if you draw it out, but you need not; all placings are in whole numbers of feet which divide into 60 exactly.

How far from the post is the nearest black ?

93

Pi Crater

Pi Crater is a large circular game reserve, in which the lion and the lizard move at constant, but very different, speeds. One day, the lion left the westernmost point in the reserve, travelling east, just as the lizard left the northernmost point, travelling south. After one hour, a tree on the perimeter of the reserve was due north of the lion and due west of the lizard; if then they had turned and moved towards each other, and if the lion had in the second hour travelled half as fast again as in the first hour, the two animals would have met at the end of the second hour. But they did no such thing: they went straight on at their accustomed speeds.

How long did the lion take to reach the easternmost point of the reserve?

94

People's Procession

The parade was the biggest in the city's history, the procession of marchers with accompanying bands stretching over a distance of just two miles as it made, at a steady pace, the long trek towards the People's Park to hear the Party Chairman's annual pep-talk.

Only a handful of security patrolmen cruised up and down, also at constant speed, from end to end of the long procession, keeping a watchful eye for any appearance of dissident demonstrators.

By the time any patrolman had gone from one end of the procession to the other and back again, it had moved forward just $1\frac{1}{2}$ miles, while he himself had covered . . .

Covered how many miles?

95

Circular Tour

Arley, Barley, Carley, Darley, Earley and Farley are six villages connected, in that order, by a circular bus service.

A passenger is allowed to board at any village and alight at any other or complete the whole circuit. The distances from any village to any other village on the route are all different and all an exact number of miles, consisting of every possible whole number from 1 mile up to the distance for the whole circuit.

Arley to Barley is 1 mile. The distance from Farley to Arley is greater than that from Barley to Carley but less than that from Earley to Farley.

What is the distance from Earley to Farley?

The Poorer the Truer

There are three tribes on the Island of Imperfection – the Pukkas, who always tell the truth; the Wotta-Woppas, who never tell the truth; and the Shilli-Shallas, who make statements which are alternately true and false, or false and true.

It is sad to record that recently the inhabitants of the island have become interested in material gain, and therefore even less perfect. The Golden Age, in fact, has been replaced by the golden wage.

The four with whom this story deals (we shall call them A, B, C and D) are all earning wages which are not less than £15 and not more than £30 a week. In every case their weekly earnings are an exact number of pounds. One of them is a Pukka, one a Wotta-Woppa and the other two are Shilli-Shallas. Their wages are all different and it happens that their truthfulness in the three remarks which are recorded below ascends as their wages descend. But whether this is cause and effect or coincidence we shall probably never know. Three of the four are married; we shall call their wives X, Y and Z in no particular order.

They make remarks as follows:

A: 1. The Wotta-Woppa's wages are 20 per cent greater than those of one of the Shilli-Shallas.
   2. The difference between my wages and B's is £10 a week.
   3. D's weekly wages are a multiple of £4.
B: 1. Z's husband's weekly wages are an even number of £s.
   2. I am a Shilli-Shalla.
   3. The best paid of us is married to X.
C: 1. One of the Shilli-Shallas' wages are 33⅓ per cent greater than those of the Pukka.
   2. The Pukka is a bachelor.
   3. B's wages are less than mine.
D: 1. The weekly wage of one of us is a prime number of pounds.

2. The difference between the weekly wages of the two Shilli-Shallas is £1.
3. One of the Shilli-Shallas is married to Z.

Find to which tribe each man belongs, his weekly wages and to whom, if anyone, he is married.

97

The ABC Club

Membership of the ABC Club is restricted to actors, brewers and criminologists. A candidate for election must pass a test which involves deducing the callings of his four inquisitors (hooded, and distinguished only by letters on their cowls) from the remarks which they make to one another. The candidate is told only: that all three callings are included in the quartet; that he must disbelieve any statement made by an actor to a criminologist, by a brewer to actor, and by a criminologist to a brewer, but that he may safely trust all other statements.

My four addressed one another as follows:

P to Q: You're a brewer.
R to Q: You're not a criminologist.
R to P: You're either a brewer or a criminologist.
S to R: You are of the same calling as P.

I managed to pass the test, and was elected. Some months later I was invited to join three of my former inquisitors on a selection board. All three in turn addressed me and said: 'You're a . . .' (mentioning one or other of the possible callings). Only *one* of their statements was true.

What am I?

98

Bouquet

Three of my friends live near by and we all grow roses. Williams goes in for standards, some crimson and some yellow. The Proctors have a pergola with ramblers, some red and some white. The Browns have a sheltered corner for their white dwarfs and they also have some rather untidy crimson bushes. In my garden I have examples of all these six varieties and in addition a speciality of my own.

All of us have families and our young children play together. It is the Williams girl who often gets up to mischief. The other morning she brought round a largish bunch of roses for my wife's birthday. On examining it I found that there were an equal number of blooms of each colour, and that she had outrageously picked an equal number of each colour in each neighbour's garden – and the rest from mine. Although my wife was touched by the friendly gesture, we were all rather cross at the child's unauthorized pilfering.

In an attempt at conciliation I asked my three friends round for drinks. I knew that each bloom of my speciality cost four times Proctor's flowers and three times one of the standards. But old Brown grumbled that his dwarfs were worth twice as much as any of the crimson roses. Williams admitted that his yellow blooms were worth only half a bush rose, and he calculated, rather sheepishly, that his little girl's effort totted up to just 26 times the cost of one rambler rose.

What colour is my speciality?

Tessie the Typist

Tessie the typist is not in great demand; unfortunately her eyes are somewhat peculiar and her figure-work is faulty.

This is no reflection on her appearance. The fact is that, when called upon to type a number, she invariably reverses the order of the digits. If, for example, the number were 1,234, Tessie would type 4,321 and, if the proper figures were 36 24 34, her version would be 63, 42, 43 – however vital the statistics might be.

On one occasion she should have typed a certain number (X) and its square (Y). The odd thing was that the number Tessie typed instead of Y was, as it happened, the square of the number she typed instead of X.

All the digits in Y were different and, when added together, totalled more than 35. Both X and Y, and also the two numbers Tessie actually typed, were *odd* (but none included 5 or 0). X was smaller than the number Tessie typed in its stead.

What number was Y?

100

Good-bye

I was leaving Bahrein Teza. With my head out of the railway carriage window I exchanged farewells with my Bahreini friend on the platform.

'Pleasant journey,' he said. 'Ring me up when you're safely home.'

'What number?' I asked, as the train gently began moving. He walked alongside.

He said, 'My number lies between 3,000 and 4,000.'

'Yes?'

'And it is the sum of three smaller numbers, one of two figures, one of three figures, and one of four figures. All the figures are different with no zero.'

'Yes?' He was walking quite quickly.

'Each of the three smaller numbers is either a factor or a multiple of the other two numbers.'

'Yes?' He was trotting.

'My number is 36 times the two-figure number.'

At this point he fell off the end of the platform. When I rang up later I was relieved to learn he wasn't much hurt.

Number please?

Solutions

1

Absentees

ANSWER

Aden, Cuff, Dudd.

SOLUTION

1. As the commander knew with certainty who the absentees were, it is evident that only one 'combination' could have been possible.
2. The seven men had a total of 28 rounds. The three sick men could not have had more than 11 rounds (which was the maximum the two off duty could have had, i.e. 28 less 17) or less than 6 (1, 2, 3).
3. The possible ways in which two men 'off duty' could have had the same number of rounds as three on duty are:

No.	3 men on	2 men off	No.	3 men on	2 men off
11	1, 3, 7	5, 6	9	1, 2, 6	4, 5
11	1, 4, 6	not possible	9	1, 3, 5	2, 7
11	2, 3, 6	4, 7	9	2, 3, 4	not possible
11	2, 4, 5	not possible	8	1, 2, 5	not possible
10	1, 2, 7	4, 6	8	1, 3, 4	2, 6
10	1, 3, 6	not possible	7	1, 2, 4	not possible
10	1, 4, 5	3, 7	6	1, 2, 3	not possible
10	2, 3, 5	4, 6			

4. Of the possible numbers, only 8 provides one, and only one, feasible combination, i.e. 1, 3, 4 for the three sick men and 2, 6 for the two men who replaced them. Thus the number of rounds carried by those on duty must have been 20, and the absentees were Aden (1 round), Cuff (3) and Dudd (4) – their replacements being Bill (2) and Ford (6).

2

South Pacific

ANSWER

Bali-Hai, 8 p.m. Thursday.

SOLUTION

Apparent travelling times for A–B, B–C and C–A are 34, 71 and 36 hours respectively, which can only be reconciled on the assumption that the three islands straddle the International Date Line, thus introducing at some point a disparity of a day. The six alternative adjustments for true travelling times are:

A–B	B–C	C–A
58	47	36
34	47	60
58	71	12
10	71	60
34	95	12
10	95	36

Each of the last four can be eliminated as a mutually incompatible trio.

Moreover the radio signal was sent 84 hours after the ferry left A and while it was 'on its course' between B and C. This eliminates the second set of figures, since the ferry would already have reached C.

The first possibility is therefore the unique solution: the signal is sent when the ferry is 23 hours out from B whither it returns after another 23 hours, i.e. 46 hours after sailing. Hence it arrives there at 8 p.m. on Thursday (in Bali-Hai = Friday in Aloha).

3

The Pay Roll Rules

Alf	Doorkeeper	£378.
Bert	Welfare Officer	£400.
Charlie	Doorknob Polisher	£468.
Duggie	Bottle Washer	£250.
Ernie	Worker	£308.

SOLUTION

1. From 2, E gets $\frac{112}{100} \times \frac{110}{100}$ (i.e. $\frac{154}{125}$) of B-W's present wage.
   This gives us the ratio of E's wage to the B-W. Since they must be whole numbers of pounds, between 200 and 600 (from 5), and since B-W's must be divisible by 10 (he gets a 10 per cent rise next month), E's wage = £308 and B-W's wage = £250.

2. From 6, D-K gets $\frac{105}{100} \times \frac{90}{100}$ (i.e. $\frac{189}{200}$) of B's wage.
   Since no wages are less than £200 or greater than £600, D-K's wage must be £378 or £567, and B's wage must be £400 or £600. And E not B-W or D-K; and B not D-K or B-W.

3. From 3, D-K-P gets $\frac{130}{100}$ (i.e. $\frac{13}{10}$) of old wage, so his wage is divisible by 13; D-K-P not B or E.

4. From 4, C gets £$(\frac{120}{100}P - 12)$ (where P is W-O's wage), i.e. C gets £$(\frac{6}{5}P - 12)$. Therefore W-O's wage is divisible by 5; so W-O not E; Thus by elimination E is W and B is W-O.

5. B's wage is £400 or £600 (see (2)). If £600, C's wage would be £$(\frac{6}{5} \times 600 - 12)$ which is more than £600. So B's wage is £400. Therefore C's wage is £$(\frac{6}{5} \times 400 - 12)$, i.e. £468. From (2) D-K's wage is £378, so C not D-K. From para. 1 B-W's wage is £250, so C not B-W. So by elimination C is D-K-P.

6. Therefore A and D are between them D-K (£378) and B-W (£250), and so from para. 1, A is D-K and D is B-W.

4

Towns and Families

The Carters were married in Belfast.

SOLUTION

The completed matrix is:

Family	Husband born	Married	Wife born
Archer	Edinburgh	London	Belfast
Drew	Belfast	Edinburgh	Cardiff
Carter	Cardiff	Belfast	London
Brewer	London	Cardiff	Edinburgh

The woman born in Belfast must be married east of her birthplace. This is also true of the woman married in London. The top line is uniquely fixed by the conditions about the Archers.

The man born in Belfast must marry in Edinburgh. This uniquely fixes the second and third columns.

The woman married in Cardiff must have been born in Edinburgh or London, but the latter is excluded by the husband's birthplace. This fixes the last column.

The Brewer condition places them on the bottom row. Mr Carter and Mrs Drew were born in the same town.

5

Book Pages

ANSWER

In the current edition 5; in the reprint 4.

SOLUTION

1. Seven pages for footnotes leave 193 for text and blank pages. A blank page follows each even-number chapter *with* notes, and each odd-number chapter *without* notes.

2. In eight consecutive numbers there are 4 evens and 4 odds. If the one chapter without footnotes
   (a) is *even*, there are three even and four odd; and three blanks;
   (b) is *odd*, there are four even and three odd; and five blanks.
   Therefore the total pages of text is 193 minus either 3 or 5.

3. The number of pages in each chapter form a sequence between 15 and 30. The only suitable one is 20 to 27. This totals 188, and there must be therefore *five* blank pages in the current edition.

4. In the reprint, by assembling the notes after chapter 8, the printer uses $3\frac{1}{2}$ pages, reducing the volume by 4 pages to 196, and leaving only *four* pages completely blank.

5. The arrangement of the two editions is clearly shown thus:

Page numbers

Current edition	Text	Notes	Blank
Chapter 1 (20)	1–20	21	22
2 (21)	23–43	44	—
3 (22)	45–66	67	68
4 (23)	69–91	92	—
5 (24)	93–116	117	118
6 (25)	119–143	144	—
7 (26)	145–170	171	172
8 (27)	173–199	—	200

current edition: 200 pp. *5 blank*

new edition: 196 pp. *4 blank*

6

Batting Averages

ANSWER

369.

SOLUTION

Let A's number of completed innings be n and his average be x; then his total of runs is nx.

Had he been given 'not out', his number of *completed* innings would have been $(n-1)$ and his average $(x+1)$: an increase from 0·5 *less* than B's to 0·5 *more*.

His total runs were unaffected by the last ball; so

$$nx = (n-1)(x+1) = nx-x+n-1$$

whence $x = n-1$.

So A's total runs $= n(n-1)$, an *even* number between 300 and 500.

But B's number of innings must be *even* and his total runs *odd* to produce an average ending ·5. As B had 3 fewer innings, then n is *odd*.

The only possible values of $n(n-1)$ are:

(a) $19 \times 18 = 342$ (b) $21 \times 20 = 420$.

For (a) B's total $= 16 \times 18·5 = 296$.   *Too small.*

   (b) „   „ $= 18 \times 20·5 = 369$.

7

Which Page ?

ANSWER

The reference was on page 198.

SOLUTION

The total of the six variants of any three-figure number is always equal to 222 times the sum of its digits.

The student misread only a single figure, so his error is an exact number of units, or an exact number of tens, or an exact number of hundreds.

To obtain a total of 4796 the only conforming arrangement is 222×18 digits $(3996) + 800 = 4796$.

This means that the hundreds figure which he mistook for a 9 was really a 1. Since the digits total 18, the other figures must be 9 and 8.

8

House-Number

420.

Suppose my house-number is x.

The numbers on my left are:
$$(x-1), (x-2), \ldots \text{etc.};$$
and on my right $(x+1), (x+2), \ldots$ etc.

Now number $(x+n)$ exceeds $(x-1)$ by $(n+1)$

$(x+n-1)$ exceeds $(x-2)$ by $(n+1)$

$(x+n-2)$ exceeds $(x-3)$ by $(n+1)$

until finally $(x+1)$ exceeds $(x-n)$ by $(n+1)$.

There are n of these differences, so the sum of n house-numbers on my right exceeds the sum of n house-numbers on my left by $n(n+1)$, and since my house-number makes up this difference
$$x = n(n+1) \ldots (1).$$

Again, $(x+1)^2$ exceeds $(x-1)^2$ by $4x$

$(x+2)^2$ exceeds $(x-2)^2$ by $8x$

until finally $(x+m)^2$ exceeds $(x-m)^2$ by $4mx$.

Therefore the total difference $= 4x(1+2+3, \ldots m)$
$$= 4x \times m \times \text{average of } 1, 2, \ldots m$$
$$= 4x \; \frac{\times m(m+1)}{2}$$
$$= 2m(m+1)x$$

Therefore $\qquad x^2 = 2m(m+1)x$

Therefore $\qquad x = 2m(m+1) \ldots (2)$

Therefore $\qquad 2m(m+1) = n(n+1) = x.$

The solutions are:
$$2.2.3 = 3.4 = 12$$
$$2.14.15 = 20.21 = 420$$
The next is $2.84.85 = 119.120 = 14,280$
from which it is clear that my number is 420.

9

Electing a Chairman

SOLUTION

Seating arrangement:

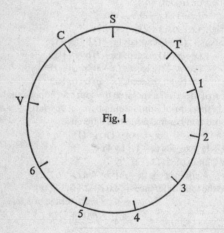

Fig. 1

Item

(1) No self vote.
(2) No vote for neighbour.
(3) No mutual pairs.
(4) No officer voting for officer.
(5) C vote vote vote 2.
(6) T vote vote vote 4.

(7) V vote vote vote 5.
(8) S vote vote vote 6.
(9) 4 did not vote for officer.
(10) C, S did not vote for 3.
(11) 6 vote vote 3 is impossible.

Suppose, after the election, all the voters form circles so that each man is to the left of the one who voted for him.

Try putting all voters in one circle. Fix T and 4 (Fig. 2). *a* not officer

136

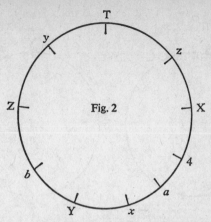

Fig. 2

by (9). So Xx, Yy, Zz are only available points for C2, V5, S6; X, Y, Z being officers, x, y, z, not officers to fit items (4) to (8).

Hence a, b are 1, 3 but $a \neq 3$ by (2)
so $b = 3$. $a = 1$ and $x \neq 2$ by (2)

By (10) $Y = V$, i.e. $y = 5$ and $x = 2$ or 6.
Both impossible by (2).

Hence we must split up our ten members into closed groups, Isolated points or pairs are eliminated by (1) and (3).

By (6) and (9) T is in a group of n where $N > 4$ i.e. $n = 5$, 6, or 7 to agree (1) and (3).

By (5) (7) and (8) C, V and S are all in groups of four or more members. Thus we have only 2 groups, either 7, 3
or 5, 5
or 6, 4

And to agree (5), (6), (7), (8)
(a) A group of 7 can only take 2 officers
(b)   ,,   ,,   ,, 6 ,,   ,,   ,, 2 ,,
(c)   ,,   ,,   ,, 5 ,,   ,,   ,, 1 ,,
(d)   ,,   ,,   ,, 4 ,,   ,,   ,, 2 ,,
(e)   ,,   ,,   ,, 3 ,, take no officers

So our groups are 6, 4 with T in the 6 group. Place T, 4; e not an officer by (9). (Figs. 3, 3a.)

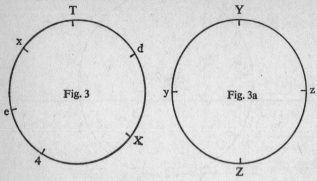

Fig. 3

Fig. 3a

As before, Xx, Yy, Zz account for C 2, V 5, S 6.
$e = 1$, $d = 3$. By (11) and by (2) x must be 5,
i.e. $X = V$
$\quad Y = C \quad y = 2$
$\quad Z = S \quad z = 6$
and the result (Figs. 4, 4a).

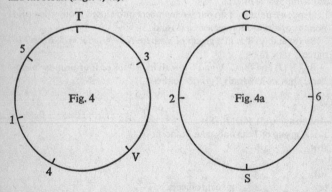

Fig. 4

Fig. 4a

Therefore the order is 6 2 3 5 C V 1 T S 4.

10

Brothers and Sisters

SOLUTION

The evidence given can be shown in a diagram as follows:

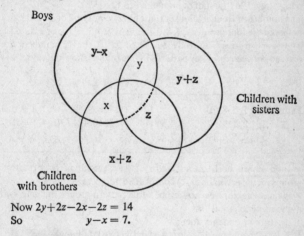

Now $2y+2z-2x-2z = 14$

So $y-x = 7$.

11

Club Lockers

No. 2.

1. Each of the 3 different keys must have fitted 4 lockers whose numbers totalled 26 (the sum of numbers 1 to 12 = 78).
2. The number of Bunker's locker must have been 1 or 2 or 11 or 12 and in one of the four groups 1, 7, 8, 10; 2, 7, 8, 9; 4, 5, 6, 11; or 3, 5, 6, 12.
3. The four 'groups' can only be 'fitted in' if the 12 numbers are divided between the 3 key patterns in one of the following ways:

	W	X	Y	Z
Pattern 1	1, 7, 8, 10	1, 7, 8, 10	2, 7, 8, 9	2, 7, 8, 9
„ 2	2, 3, 9, 12	2, 4, 9, 11	1, 3, 10, 12	1, 4, 10, 11
„ 3	4, 5, 6, 11	3, 5, 6, 12	4, 5, 6, 11	3, 5, 6, 12

4. W and Z are both unsatisfactory because each of their pattern groups includes two or more consecutive numbers.
5. X is unsatisfactory because none of its pattern groups includes two numbers which total 16.
6. Y meets requirements since:
   1, 3, 10, 12 could have pattern A keys (no two adjoining).
   7 and 8 or 8 and 9 could be Pitcher's and Putter's lockers (adjoining).
   5 (lower than 7, 8 or 9) will be Wedge's and 11 Wood's (total 16).
   2 will be Bunker's (7 is further from 2 than are 1, 3, 4, 5 and 6).

12

Hymn Numbers

ANSWER

No. 529.

SOLUTION

The only 18 hymn numbers eligible through being square and their digits also totalling to a square are:

001	004		036	009	100
081	144	225	196	169	
121	324				
441	484			529	400
961					900

Consider which of these are eligible for the *final* (Row 4) hymn number, bearing in mind

(a) that no squares end in 2, 3, 7 or 8, and
(b) that the penultimate digit of squares ending in
   (i) 0, is 0
   (ii) 5, is 2
   (iii) 6, is an *odd* number
   (iv) 1, 4 or 9, is an *even* number.

Now since the final two digits of Row 3 are stated to be 0, it is clear from the above that the final two digits of Row 4, for Cols. 2 and 3 both to be square, can only comprise 0, 1, 4 and 9, and, for Row 4 to be square, must therefore be

–00, –01, –04, –09, –41, –44, or –49.

–00 can be ruled out since, using the only available numbers to make the figures in Cols. 2 and 3 both square, the sole possibility is

4	4	1
1	9	6
4	0	0
1/9	0	0

in which, however, Col. 1 is *not* a square (63^2 being $3^2 \times 21^2 = 9 \times 441$, i.e. only 3,969, and 67^2 obviously far greater than 4,149).

–01, *–04* and *–09* can also be ruled out since the only eligible squares for Row 4 would all require 0 as the first digit and therefore, to make Col. 1 square, as the first digit of Row 3 also – which is impossible.

–49 can also be ruled out since there is no eligible square with this ending.

There remain only *–41* and *–44*, and the only two possibilities for Rows 3 and 4 giving a square ending for Col. 1 are 4 0 0 and 4 0 0
$$4\ 4\ 1 \qquad 1\ 4\ 4.$$
Now Col. 2 divided by Row 4 is stated to yield a square, and if Row 4 is 441 ($= 21^2$), only 42^2 ($= 4 \times 441$) could yield a 4-digit square ending in *–4*, and its penultimate digit is 6, not the required 0.

However, if Row 4 is 144 ($= 12^2$), 4-digit squares ending in *–4* would result from squaring either 48 or 72 and would be respectively (16×144) and (36×144). But 36 cannot be the digital total of a 3-digit number; the only possibility for Col. 2 is therefore 16×144, i.e. 2,304, and for Row 2 is 036, thus:

```
  2
0 3 6
4 0 0
1 4 4
```

Hence it has to be Row 1 which has the digital total of 16, and the only such square with 2 as its middle digit is 529.

N.B. 5041 and 9604 in Cols. 1 and 3 are the squares of 71 and 98 respectively.

Note: Though this three-tier problem can, as indicated in its wording, be solved at three different stages, this solution makes use of all the clues given.

13

Our Factory on the Cricket Field

ANSWER

Alf, opening bat, 37 runs.
Bert, leg-break bowler, 32 runs, 4 wickets.
Charlie, wicket-keeper, 27 runs.
Duggie, fast bowler, 64 runs, 4 wickets.
Ernie, umpire.

SOLUTION

It is helpful to have a table, using obvious abbreviations, in which information can be inserted as obtained. Thus:

	x 1-b-b	√x f-b	√x o-b	√ w-k	√ ump
A					
B					
C					
D					
E					

(√s and xs represent data about truth-telling.

D1, 3 and 5 are all true or all false (see conditions about truth-telling).

Suppose all true. Then A is w-k (D5), so A's remarks all true, so two of opposition were run out (A3).

But C and E took 9 wickets between them (D1 and 3). This makes 11 wickets altogether, which is impossible. Therefore D1, 3, 5 are all false. So A not w-k, and since D makes false remarks, D not w-k or ump. So E1 is true, so E3 is true, so E not l-b-b.

A scored 37, so A not ump.

Since E not l-b-b, A1 is true, so A3 is true. Therefore A not l-b-b.

Since, by elimination, A must be either f-b or o-b, A2 is false, so C's score is a multiple of 9. So C is not ump.

Suppose B1 is true; then B3 is true.

C's score would be a multiple of 63, and D could not have scored 10 per cent more than C (no one scores more than 100, and all scores must obviously be whole numbers). B1 and B3 are thus false, so B not w-k or ump. Therefore by elimination E is ump, and then, by elimination, C is w-k. So C's statements and E's statements are all true.

From E2 D not o-b.

Since A3 is true, bowlers took not more than 8 wickets.

From E2, D took more than 3 wickets; from C1 f-b and l-b-b took same number of wickets; so each took 4 wickets, so from E4, B scored 32.

B2 cannot be true, for D would have scored more than 100. So B's remarks all false, so B is l-b-b. So by elimination A is o-b, and D is f-b.

D2 is true, so C's score less than 31 and a multiple of 9.

D4 is true; so D's score a perfect square (C2), and equal to total of two other scores.

The only possibility is for C's score to be 27, and for D's to be 64 (37+27).

14

Midsummer Birthday Madness

ANSWER

11 June 1954.

SOLUTION

1. The birth dates and ages are:

2.6.60	2
7.6.55	7
11.6.54	8
17.5.58	4
24.6.61	1
25.6.61	0
28.6.58	3
28.6.56	5
30.6.55	6

2. The twins are John and his sister, who was born just after midnight, i.e. on 25 June.
3. The total of ages of the first four, first three, last four and last three are respectively 21, 17, 14 and 14. The ages in ascending date order are 2, 7, 8, 4, 1 and 0 followed by 3, 5, and 6 in an unknown order.
4. The birthday intervals easily fix the dates at 2, 7, 11, 17, 24, 25, 28, 28 and 30. (111 = 3 × 37.)

15

Electric Clock

ANSWER

12 September.

SOLUTION

1. The clock loses an additional minute each 24 hours from the noon when I found it one minute slow 'towards the end of August'. At noon on 1 September the clock shows a loss of 21 minutes, which must be the sum of the series 1 – 2 – 3 – 4 . . . In fact, the sum of 1, 2, 3, 4, 5, 6 is 21, and the loss for the 24 hours to noon on 1 September is therefore the last of this series – six minutes.

2. When I left home on 1 September I set the hands at noon, but the clock (for the battery cannot be rewound) will continue to run at the accumulated loss rate for each 24-hour period in the series 7 – 8 – 9 . . . The maximum possible loss for a whole fortnight is the sum of this series for 14 days, that is 169 minutes. As I returned early the loss must be less than this.

3. On my return the hands of my watch were overlapping and those of my clock nearly so. The time between any three moments when the hands overlap (and when I put the clock right the hands crossed three times) is a little under 2 hours and 11 minutes. By reference to the sum of the series above it will be seen that a loss of exactly 2 hours and 12 minutes (132 minutes) occurred at noon on the seventeenth day. When my watch showed exactly noon the clock stood at 9.48. It took me one minute to change the battery (the correct time being then 12.01), and in setting the clock right the hands crossed at 9.49, 10.54, and at noon.

4. The date of my return was therefore the seventeenth day from the time when the clock began to lose, 12 September.

16

Common Frontier

134 Emils per hour.

SOLUTION

Call the Europhalian counting-base E and the Sopiculian S. The weight-ratios given by the two informants must be equal; so

$$\frac{4E+2}{2E+4} = \frac{2S+6}{S+6}$$

$(4E+2)(S+6) = (2E+4)(2S+6)$

$4ES+24E+2S+12 = 4ES+12E+8S+24$

$12E-6S = 12$

$2E-S = 2.$

S is less than 10, and greater than 6 (since the S man uses 6 as a digit in his notation). S must be *even*, or E would be fractional. So S = 8, whence E = 5.

21 on the E system = 11 to base 10; 21 on S system = 17 base 10. Therefore the Emil is $\frac{17}{11}$ Somils.

104 Somils expressed in denary notation is $64+0+4 = 68$ units.

Same length in Emils ,,   ,,   ,,   is $68 \times \frac{11}{17} = 44$ units.

On the Europhalian system (base 5) the denary number 44 would be written 134 ($25+3\times5+4$).

17

Antics

39 feet.

SOLUTION

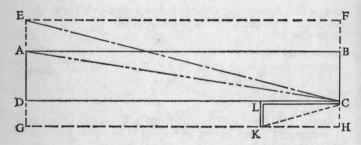

The key to the solution lies in the movements of Taran and Tula (see KLC). This being an integral right-angled triangle, possible dimensions are easily found (sides must all be multiples of 5 with KL ⩽ 30 feet). It will be seen that the Run time difference between KC and LC must be made up by the Drop time of KL (the wall).

The only possibilities are

	KC	LC	Drop Time	KL wall	AC	EC (see below)*
(a)	25 ft	20 ft	1 second	15 ft	215 ft	220 ft
(b)	25 ,,	15 ,,	2 ,,	20 ,,	210 ,,	220 ,,
(c)	65 ,,	60 ,,	1 ,,	25 ,,	255 ,,	260 ,,
(d)	50 ,,	40 ,,	2 ,,	30 ,,	235 ,,	245 ,,

Now, as Taran finishes level with Ara at equal speed the distance KC is the same for both.

* So AC is 5(39−Drop time)+ KC feet,

* and EC is AC+Run distance covered by Chne during Ara's Drop time.

Call width of corridor x and length y.

Then $EC^2 = y^2 + (\text{wall} + x)^2$ and $AC^2 = y^2 + x^2$,

so $EC^2 - AC^2 = \text{wall}^2 + 2x \text{ wall}$,

so $x = \dfrac{(EC^2 - AC^2) - \text{wall}^2}{2 \text{ wall}}$. See (a) (b) (c) (d) above for detail.

(a) $x = \dfrac{2075 - 225}{30} = 65$ feet, and $y = 204 \cdot 9$ feet (inadmissible).

(b) $x = \dfrac{4300 - 400}{40} = 93\frac{1}{2}$ feet (inadmissible).

(c) $x = \dfrac{2575 - 625}{50} = 39$ feet and $y = 252$ feet.

(d) $x = \dfrac{4800 - 900}{60} = 65$ feet and $y = 225 \cdot 8$ feet (inadmissible).

So $x = 39$ feet.

18

Birthday Party

ANSWER

Adam died in 1953 and was then 96 years old.

SOLUTION

Let the ages at the first party in descending order be A, E, J, D.

Then $A+E+J = x^2$

$A+E+D = y^2$

$A+J+D = z^2$

$E+J+D = w^2$

Adding, $3(A+E+J+D) = x^2+y^2+z^2+w^2$,

so $x^2+y^2+z^2+w^2$ is a multiple of 3.

The only squares we need consider are 81, 100, 121, 144, 169, 196.

To make a multiple of 3 we must include 100, 121, and 169 or 196.

Consider 100, 121, 144, 169.

Then $3(A+E+J+D) =$ 534

So $A+E+J+D =$ 178;

but $A+E+J =$ 169

so $D = 9$

$A+E+D = 144,$

so $J = 34.$

$A+J+D = 121,$

so $E = 57$

and $A = 78.$

At the next party, E, J and D are each the same number of years older and the sum of their ages is another square, greater than 100 by a multiple of 3.

This sum must be 196.

So they are each 32 years older:

so E is 89, J is 66, D is 41.

The new youngest member S must be 14, so Adam died in 1953 and his age was $78+32-14 = 96$.

19
Space Ship

ANSWER

AE and AF.

SOLUTION

There are 36 crew. We have listed them below in 4 groups and we see that a prole, if there were no officers, would hand over to the one named to his right in the table. To use up all the proles there must be the same number of officers from each group. This means there must be AD, BC given, and EI, FH. These have been marked in brackets.

Group 1	AB	(BC)	CD	DE	EF	FG	GH	HI	IA
„ 2	AC	BD	CE	DF	EG	(FH)	GI	HA	IB
„ 3	(AD)	BE	CF	DG	EH	FI	GA	HB	IC
„ 4	AE	BF	CG	DH	(EI)	FA	GB	HC	ID

Two shifts are insufficient but we could have 8 or 4 shifts, the latter giving our answer. For the first shift take in each group the first and fifth names after the officers, that is CD GH GI BD BE FI FA AE.

20

Veres and Ficts

Alan is a Fiver, Bruce a Verific, Carl a Fict and David a Vere. The Prince is a Fiver.

SOLUTION

1. As Carl says he is a Verific, he must be a Fict. So the Prince is *not* a Fict.
2. So Alan's first statement is a lie. Alan cannot be the Fict (since C is the Fict child) and so is the Fiver. Therefore Alan's mother is a Vere, whence the Prince's cook is a Vere.
3. Now either Bruce or David must be the Vere child. If Bruce is the Vere (and David the Verific), it follows that the Prince's father is a Fict (from B1, B2 and D1), but also that the Prince's father is a Vere (since D2 has to be a lie). Therefore Bruce is *not* the Vere.
4. As David is the Vere, it follows that the Prince's father is a Fict (D2). We already know that the Prince is not a Fict; so he must be a Fiver.

21
Absorbers

ANSWER

Extra dry sherry; lemon; soda water.

SOLUTION

1. Medium sherry (MS) did not go with (X) lemon or (Y) dry ginger, leaving (X) tonic and vermouth and (Y) plain water and soda to be considered.
2. Dry sherry (DS) did not go with (X) vermouth or (Y) plain water, leaving (X) tonic and lemon and (Y) soda and dry ginger as possibles.
3. Extra dry sherry (EDS) could not have gone with tonic (since tonic went with medium or dry sherry) leaving (X) lemon and vermouth as possibles.
4. Summarized and using initials, the position is

   Possibles

1		2	3
MS	with	T or V	PW or SW
DS	„	T or L	SW or DG
EDS	„	L or V	PW or SW or DG

5. There are only two possible combinations for column 2, i.e. with MS, DS and EDS respectively either (i) tonic, lemon and vermouth or (ii) vermouth, tonic and lemon.
6. Arrangement (i) would put medium sherry with tonic and thus with soda water (tonic and plain water did not go together, i.e. only one of the two was a member of the A.A.). This would leave dry sherry to go with lemon and dry ginger. This, however, is not acceptable since lemon and dry ginger have nothing in common.
7. This means that the only acceptable arrangement is:

   Medium sherry and vermouth and plain water (soda did not go with vermouth).
   Dry sherry and tonic and dry ginger.
   Extra dry sherry and lemon and soda water.

8. As neither the taker of vermouth nor the selector of soda was a representative of B.B., that concern must have employed the dry sherry group.
9. As either the taker of tonic or of plain water was a member of the A.A., that concern must have the medium sherry group.
10. This leaves the C.C. with the extra dry sherry group – which includes lemon and soda water.

22

Billiard Balls

ANSWER

(i) 6 weighings; (ii) 26 balls.

SOLUTION

The largest number of balls from which the single reject ball could be identified in *five* weighings is 120, and uniquely the same technique could, in *six* weighings, deal with as many as 363 balls. There are nevertheless four (at least) different approaches which Bill could, in a total of six weighings, use towards identifying the reject ball out of as small a total number as $(14 \times 12) + 1$, i.e. *169*, but only two of these programmes would involve the weighing of as few as 250 balls in all.

The standard approach would be to separate the 169 balls into seven lots as under:

(a)	(b)	(c)	(d)	(e)	(f)	(g)
43	43	42	27	9	3	2

One (extreme) example of a succession of weighings and outcomes which would lead to a total of 250 balls weighed is as follows:

1. 43 ◄──► 43

2. 42 ◄────────► 42

3. 27 ◄────────────► 27

4. 9 ◄────────────────────► 9

5. 3 ◄────────────────────────► 3

6. ↓1

$125 \times 2 = \underline{250}$

But it is clear that, once the first two weighings have proved to be in balance, the succeeding ones *must* comprise respectively 2×27, 2×9, 2×3 and 2×1 balls, and Bill could *already* tell that the balls weighed would total 250 in all.

There is, however, a second alternative approach to the task. The problem is to identify the reject ball out of a total which happens to equal 13^2, and advantage can be taken of the fact that it is possible, in *three* weighings, to identify a 'maverick' among *13* single balls, not 12 as commonly believed. The technique is as follows:

The balls should be divided up into three groups of 5, 4 and 4 respectively which we may identify by the letters abcde, fghi and jklm. The first weighing must be fghi *v*. jklm.

Case 1. If they balance, the reject is one of a, b, c, d, e. Hence second weighing must be abc *v*. 3 good balls (e.g. fgh).

Case 1a. If these balance, weigh d *v*. a good ball (e.g. f).

Case 1b. If abc proves heavy (or light) weigh a *v*. b. This establishes which of the 3 is the heavy (or light) ball.

Case 2. If fghi prove, say, heavier than jklm, second weighing must be fghj *v*. i + 3 good balls (say abc).

Case 2a. If these balance, k, l or m must be light; hence weigh k *v*. l to determine which of the 3 is the light ball.

Case 2b. If fghj is heavier than iabc, then f, g or h must be heavy. Hence weigh f *v*. g to determine which of the 3 is the heavy ball.

Case 2c. If fghj is lighter than iabc, then either j is light or i is heavy. Hence weigh i (or j) against a good ball (e.g. f) to determine which.

Now clearly this same technique can be used to identify one of 13 *groups* of equal size whose weight is uniquely different from that of the rest; thus 169 balls can be divided into 13 groups of 13 balls each in order to establish (as above) which group contains the non-standard ball. This requires, as already seen, only three weighings, and a further three weighings using the 13 balls of the now identified non-standard group then permits identification of the reject ball.

The only combination of cases which could lead to the use (in the six weighings together) of 250 balls in all is Case 2 applied to the 13 *groups* of 13 followed by Case 1 applied to the *single* balls, and, while Bill would know after the very first weighing that he would require to use in all either 250 *or* 252 balls, he would not know until the fourth weighing whether Case 1 or again Case 2 was going to apply to the single balls and therefore whether 250 or 252 balls would be involved. In either event, only 2×13 balls, i.e. 26, are used in the third weighing. An example succession of weighings and outcomes leading to the use of 250 balls would be:

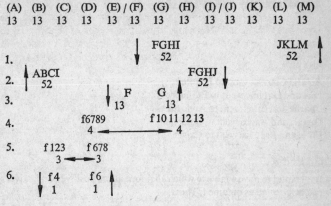

(A)	(B)	(C)	(D)	(E) / (F)	(G)	(H)	(I) / (J)	(K)	(L)	(M)
13	13	13	13	13 13	13	13	13 13	13	13	13

1.   FGHI   JKLM
                                           52   52

2.   ABCI   FGHJ
      52   52

3.   F   G
                         13   13

4.   f6789   f 10 11 12 13
            4   ←→   4

5.   f 123   f 678
      3   ←→   3

6.   f 4   f 6
       1   1

Total balls used $= 2(52+52+13+4+3+1) = 250$.

Holidays Abroad

ANSWER

Alf and Clarissa went to Dunkirk.
Bert and Daphne went to Ethiopia.
Charlie and Ethel went to Andorra.
Duggie and Agnes went to Boulogne.
Ernie and Beatrice went to Calais.

SOLUTION

It is helpful to have a table in which all information, positive or negative, can be inserted as obtained. Thus:

		Wives					Places			
		A	B	C	D	E	a	b	c	d	e
Wives	A	x				x	x				
	B		x			x		x			
	C	x	x	x	x	√			x		
	D				x	x				x	
	E					x					x
Places	a	x									
	b		x								
	c			x							
	d				x						
	e					x					

Since of each married couple one member is truthful, and the other lies, what anyone says that his or her partner says must be false. So from what Clarissa says Ethel is married to Charlie.

(This information has been inserted in table, together with the resultant information that Ethel and Charlie are not married to anyone else. The reader is recommended to insert similar information as it is obtained.)

Therefore Charlie and Ethel didn't go to Calais or Ethiopia.

But Daphne said that Charlie went to Ethiopia, so Daphne is a liar. Therefore Beatrice did not go to Dunkirk and Alf is a liar.

And since Alf and Daphne are both liars they are not married to each other. Beatrice said she was not married to Alf. If Beatrice *is* married to Alf she tells the truth (for Alf is a liar), so she couldn't say she was *not* married to Alf if she were. So she is *not* married to Alf and Beatrice tells the truth. By elimination Alf is married to Clarissa, and Alf and Clarissa couldn't have gone to Andorra or Calais.

Since Alf is a liar, Clarissa tells the truth, so Duggie went to Boulogne, and Duggie is not married to Beatrice and Daphne did not go to Boulogne.

By elimination Ernie is married to Beatrice and therefore they didn't go to Boulogne or Ethiopia.

By elimination, Duggie is married to Agnes, and since Duggie went to Boulogne Agnes did too.

By elimination Bert is married to Daphne, so they didn't go to Boulogne or Dunkirk.

Since Beatrice tells the truth and is married to Ernie, Ernie is a liar. Therefore Charlie did not go to Dunkirk.

By elimination Charlie went to Andorra, so Ethel (his wife) went to Andorra.

Again by elimination, Beatrice went to Calais, so Ernie went to Calais too.

By elimination Bert and Daphne went to Ethiopia.

By elimination Alf and Clarissa went to Dunkirk.

24

Rugby Results

ANSWER

A beat B by 5 points to 3.

SOLUTION

The full set of results is:

	A	B	C	D	E
A	–	5	5	3	–
B	3	–	5	5	3
C	5	5	–	0	5
D	0	0	5	–	–
E	–	0	3	–	–

1. B and C have beaten E by 0–3 and 3–5. (Order not yet known.)
2. D has won 1 match and lost 2; the scores being 5–0, 0–3 and 0–5.
3. A has scored in its three matches; the scores being 5–5, 5–3 and 3–0, the last being against D.
4. C either scored 3 goals (5 points), or 5 tries (3 points). The other teams' 'against' scores show that C's scores were 5, 5, 5 and 0. C beat E by 5–3, and lost to D by 0–5. C drew 5–5 with both A and B.
5. The remaining scores are easy to deduce.

25

Ups and Downs

SOLUTION

1. Call the Ups, Downs and Levels respectively A, B, and C and the originating number x. Each messenger has a neighbour of a different clan and the chain can be regarded as a series of pairs. In order to represent each clan in the proportion $3:2:1$ there must be at least three pairs, each pair giving the following modifications of x:

   AB (or BA) pass on $\frac{15}{16}$ of x.

   AC (or CA) pass on $\frac{5}{4}$ of x.

   BC (or CB) pass on $\frac{3}{4}$ of x.

2. For a minimum chain of 6 messengers under these conditions, the groupings can only be:

(1) 3A 2B 1C which is	AB AB AC	which results in $1125/1024x$
(2) 3A 1B 2C	AB AC AC	$375/256x$
(3) 2A 3B 1C	AB AB BC	$675/1024x$
(4) 2A 1B 3C	AC AC BC	$300/256x$
(5) 1A 3B 2C	AB CB CB	$135/256x$
(6) 1A 2B 3C	AC BC BC	$180/256x$.

3. Further calculations are unnecessary, for observation at once shows that chain (4) gives the result of 300 for an originating order of 256. My own first order in January of 256 (the figure used by my predecessor) gave a delivery of only 180 plants, indicating that the messengers were now in chain (6). This was confirmed in February, giving a shortfall from my requirement of 600 for the two months of 240.

4. To remedy this shortfall in four months, as well as receiving my normal 300 a month, I must have arranged for a surplus of at least 60 a month. Chain (2) will give an adequate surplus and I accordingly changed a C and a B in Chain (6) for two As. In four months to June, I therefore received 300 extra plants, which covered my shortfall during the first two months and left me with 60 plants in hand.

26

Square Meals

Tilly Chuff: £42·05.

SOLUTION

Work in units of 5p.

Husband buying h tins at h units each spent h^2 units.

Wife   ,,   w ,,   ,, w ,,   ,,   ,, w^2 units.

£6·00 = 120 units; $120 = h^2 - w^2 = (h+w)(h-w)$.

Since $(h+w)+(h-w) = 2h$, we seek pairs of factors of 120 whose sum is even. These are 60/2, 30/4, 20/6, 12/10.

We can thus pair off the eight people and apply to the table these facts:

1. Cost: S = Mr D (must be 169).
2. Cost: Q less than 10 (must be 1).
3. Tins: H + Mrs B + Mr C = T + R + Mrs A (must be 31 + 17 + 1 = 29 + 13 + 7).
4. Cost: E + F = H + Mrs C. (After filling in 1 to 3 above, this must be 961 + 169 = 289 + 841.)
5. Cost: T more than F's wife. (And G is 4th husband.)

No. of tins x cost each	TOTAL	1	2	3	leads to	4	5
31^2	961			H/C	C	E/F C	EC
29^2	841			T/R A/C	T/R C	T/R C	TC
17^2	289			H/C	HA	HA	HA
13^2	169	S	S	SA	SA	SA	SA
13^2	169	D	D	D	D	E/F D	FD
7^2	49	D	D	T/R D	T/R D	T/R D	RD
11^2	121			B	B	B	GB
1^2	1		Q	QB	QB	QB	QB

27

Here and There

ANSWER

Aunt Jill is 34 years old.

SOLUTION

B is Bill's age number, T is Twin age number.

1. The double journey (car and bike) takes 12 hours. With no pauses this is shared 3 hours car and 9 hours bike = 108 miles.
2. So T hour to B hour a.m. (a whole number) cannot exceed 3 hours. But neither can it be less, since, if it were 2 hours, that would leave Tom with 10 hours to cycle 72 miles, with impossibly long meal breaks. So Bill is 3 years older than Twins, i.e. $B-T = 3$.
3. Car time is $(B-T)$ hours less B minutes because it starts *after* T hour, and also less T minutes because it arrives *before* B hour = $(B-T)$ hours$-(B+T)$ minutes = $60(B-T)-(B+T)$ minutes = $59(B-T)-2T$ minutes = $177-2T$ minutes.
4. The distance travelled must be less than 108 miles. Diminish this 3 miles at a time and test 105, 102 miles, etc. (1 mile at a time would involve the car in fractions of a minute.)
5. 105 miles at 36 m.p.h. = 175 mins. = $177-2T$ min. So T = 1, B = 4. 1·4 a.m. No 'sunny morning'.
   102 miles at 36 m.p.h. = 170 mins. = $177-2T$ min. So $T = 3\frac{1}{2}$ (inadmissible).
   99 miles at 36 m.p.h. = 165 mins. = $177-2T$ mins. So T = 6, B = 9.
   Start is at 9 minutes past 6 a.m. Arrival 6 minutes to 9 a.m.
6. The car has taken $2\frac{3}{4}$ hours, leaving $9\frac{1}{4}$ hours for Tom, but at 12 m.p.h. he requires only $8\frac{1}{4}$ hours to do 99 miles, and can afford an hour for pauses. This hour is taken up with 10 minutes' welcome, 6 minutes Sue, so 44 minutes Sam.
7. With distance from Here to There 99 miles, family ages are:

Sam	Jill	Bill	Sue	Sally	
44	34	9	6	6	= 99 years.

28

Rectangular Blocks

ANSWER

Dimensions are 19 in., 10 in., 7 in., and 17 in., 14 in., 5 in.

SOLUTION

If x, y, z and a, b, c represent the dimensions of the two blocks, c being the smallest:

$$x+y+z = a+b+c$$
$$xy+yz+zx = ab+bc+ca$$
$$\text{and} \qquad xyz = abc+140$$

If we diminish all the dimensions by 5 in., simple algebra will show that all these conditions still hold; but the volume of the smaller block will now be zero as $c-5 = 0$. Therefore the volume of the other becomes 140 cu. in. The possible factors are given in the table:

X = x−5 =	14	10	7	70	35	28	20	14
Y = y−5 =	5	7	5	2	4	5	7	10
Z = z−5 =	2	2	4	1	1	1	1	1
X+Y+Z =	21	19	16	73	40	34	28	29
XY+YZ+ZX =	108	104	83	212	179	173	167	155

If $A = a-5$ and $B = b-5$, the only possible values are

$$A+B = 21 = 12+9$$
$$AB = 108 = 12\times9.$$

Therefore the dimensions are 19 in., 10 in., 7 in., and 17 in., 14 in., 5 in.

29

Blocks

The blocks are arranged 3, 1, 1, 4, 8, 8, 8, 8, 3, 4, 3.

The method of arriving at this answer, and at the answers to other problems of this kind, combines common sense, intuition, and a sort of inspired trial-and-error. To explain it briefly would be impossible; to describe it in detail would be tedious.

30

Leanda

ANSWER

Five men will be able to watch from the shore; of these, one will watch both races.

SOLUTION

1. Each race has three possible results: Boat A wins, Boat B wins, or dead heat. Therefore two races yield nine possible results: A+A, A+B, A+DH, B+A, B+B, B+DH, DH+A, DH+B, DH+DH. There cannot therefore be more than nine men in the village, or the results could not establish which man was the Bloo.

2. No more than three men must be in Boat A for Race 1; in Race 2, one of these must be in B, and one not racing. Similarly, in Race 2, the three men in Boat A must come from B, and from 'not racing'. The same argument applies to Boat B.

3. If there are eight men and nine women in the village, there will not be enough women to limit the number of men in each crew to three. If there are fewer, the boats cannot be raced at all.

4. Therefore there are nine men and ten women in the village. Five women are in each crew for each race. One man does not race at all (and is the Bloo if both races are dead heats); four men miss one race each, either before or after being in Boat A or Boat B.

31

Nine Holes

280, 357, 420.

SOLUTION

1. The formation of the triangles may be summarized thus:

Hole nos.				Corresponding pars		
1	4	7	= X	5	4	4
2	5	8	= Y	4	3	3
3	6	9	= Z	5	4	5
= A	B	C	= 3,360 yds.			

2. A, B and C are in the ratio 5:3:4, which means lengths of 1,400:840: 1,120 yds (the total being 3,360 yds).

3. It is known that either hole No. 5 or hole No. 8 is 168 yds, and this length would be one of the components either of 840 or 1120 yds.

4. Testing will show that 840 yds can be divided to give a right-angled triangle measuring 357:315:168 yds.

5. It is also known that either hole No. 1 or hole No. 3 or hole No. 9 is 476 yards. Testing will show that 1,120 can be divided 476:420:224 yds.

6. These lengths will only fit into the 'pattern of pars' as holes Nos. 9, 7 and 8 respectively. Hole No. 5 must therefore be 168 yds, giving a length of 280 yds for hole No. 2.

7. We can now form a pattern:

(1)	(4)	(7)
—	—	420
(2)	(5)	(8)
280	168	224
(3)	(6)	(9)
—	—	476
1400	840	1120
A	B	C

with the further knowledge that holes Nos. 4 and 6 may be 357 and 315 yards or 315 yards and 357 yards respectively.

8. It can now be found that 1,400 is divisible 595:525:280, and it requires little further study to complete the pattern.

(1)	(4)	(7)	
525	315	420	= 1260 X
(2)	(5)	(8)	
280	168	224	= 672 Y
(3)	(6)	(9)	
595	357	476	= 1428 Z
1400	840	1120	= 3,360 yds
A	B	C	

32

Peace Talks

ANSWER

8 VSNNSVUU (senior).

SOLUTION

The number of N delegates (who are seated together) cannot be 5 or more since every fifth man could not then be U or S. Thus the number of delegates from each party must be 4, 3 or 2.

Consider each in turn, numbering the positions clockwise round the table starting from the left of the senior U delegate, and placing the four U/S selectees.

4 × 4 delegates. Positions 5, 10, 15 and 4 must all be U/S. Since 16 is U, the U block could not reach beyond 3; thus 4 and 5 would have to be S, which is impermissible.

4 × 3 delegates. Positions 5, 10, 3 and 9 must all be U/S, but 9 has to be N/V, which is impossible.

4 × 2 delegates. Positions 5, 2, 8 and 7 must all be U/S, and the U positions must therefore be 7 and 8, with S 2 and 5. N can only therefore be 3 and 4, with V 1 and 6.

Thus there are 8 delegates seated V/S/N/N/S/V/U/U.

33

Light on the Matches

	A	B	C	D	E	F
A	X	X	4–1	X	X	0–1
B	X	X	0–3	0–1	1–0	0–0
C	1–4	3–0	X	5–0	5–3	0–0
D	X	1–0	0–5	X	X	0–0
E	X	0–1	3–5	X	X	0–1
F	1–0	0–0	0–0	0–0	1–0	X

SOLUTION

A diagram will help.

	A	B	C	D	E	F
A	X	X	✓	X	X	✓
B	X	X	✓			✓
C	✓	✓	X	✓	✓	✓
D	X		✓	X		✓
E	X		✓		X	✓
F	✓	✓	✓	✓	✓	X

1. F played 5 and got 7 points; so either 3 W, 1 Dr, 1 L; or 2W, 3 Dr. But as it is not possible to win 3 matches and only score 2 goals F had 2 W, 3 Dr. Scores must have been 1–0, 1–0, 0–0, 0–0, 0–0; but we cannot tell yet which were the 2 sides against which F won.

2. C lost 1 match and got 7 points. So C must have played everyone (5 matches) with 3 W, 1 Dr, 1 L.

   Therefore C and F played everyone, and A, who only played 2 matches, played no one else.

(The facts discovered so far about who played whom have been inserted in the diagram; the reader is advised to insert other facts as they are discovered in his own diagram.)

3. Total of A, B, C, D, F matches is 19. Total of all matches must be even, since each match occurs twice. So E played an odd number – not 1 as C and F played everyone, and not 5 as E did not play A. Therefore 3. So 11 matches were played.

B played 4 matches, and since B did not play A, B played C, D, E, F. So E's matches were against B, C and F; and E did not play D. We know now who played whom.

4. Eleven matches are played and 2 points are awarded for each match, so the total of points is 22. Total so far is 20 (3+7+3+7), and since we know that A won 1 match, A must have got *2 points*, and E *none*.

5. A *v.* F must be lost (F lost none), so the score was 0–1 (see 1), so A *v.* C was a win and the score 4–1.

6. C lost 1, drew 1 and won 3. The lost match was *v.* A, and the drawn match must have been *v.* F (F lost none) and the score in C *v.* F was 0–0 (see 1). And C won against B, D, and E.

7. D played 3 and got 3 points; one match (*v.* C) was lost, so D won 1 and drew 1. D cannot have won *v.* F, who lost no matches, so D *v.* B was won and D *v.* F drawn. D scored only 1 goal, so D *v.* B was 1–0, D *v.* F was 0–0 and D *v.* C was 0–5.

8. E scored no points and so lost their 3 matches (*v.* B, C and F). E *v.* F must have been 0–1 (see 1), and F *v.* B must have been 0–0 (see 1).

9. B scored only 1 goal, so the score in B *v.* E (which B won) was 1–0. Therefore the score in B's fourth match (*v.* C) was 0–3.

10. C had 7 goals against, 4 by C, 0 by B, 0 by D, 0 by F, therefore 3 by E. E had 7 goals against, 1 by B and 1 by F, therefore 5 by C.

34

Commuters and Crosswords

ANSWER

I am Robinson and I enter fifth.

SOLUTION

1. The full order is:

Jones
Smith   puzzler
John Smith   puzzler
Brown
Robinson
Robert Brown
Bernard Jones   puzzler
Sam Robinson   puzzler.

2. For Smith and Brown to be seated together always the order includes the sequence Smith, puzzler, Brown. This is upset by the puzzler getting out of line. This puzzler is John.
3. These two puzzlers must be isolated from other puzzlers by three non-puzzlers. Smith's position in the queue must be even: it can only be second, the last two in the queue being puzzlers.
4. Jones must be first. John's father preceded him, i.e. is Smith.
5. Bernard's uncle is Robinson, whose son is Sam. Bernard is Jones's son.
6. Robert is Brown's son, and sixth. Sam and Bernard both enter after Robinson, who is fifth.

35

Nuns

ANSWER

Italian and American.

SOLUTION

1. The aircraft holds 22 passengers. As there are equal numbers of each nationality and the problem refers to 'my lady compatriots' there must be three of each nationality – there is no room for more.

2. There are four unmarried persons and therefore seven married couples. As only two nationalities are *all* married (six people) the other four couples must be equally divided between the remaining nationalities. It follows that each of the four unmarried persons must be one of these four nationalities.

3. As the sexes are equally divided the single persons must be two females (the nuns) and two males. The males are the Swede (the divorced film star) and the unmarried brother of the American's spouse (who cannot be Italian, for the Contessa has only one brother, who is married). The unmarried Italian must therefore be female, and thus one of the nuns.

4. All the British are married, and we know that a Swede, two Americans and two Italians are married to other nationals. The only other group which can all be married (including one pair married within the group) must be either German or Greek.

5. If the American is married to a Greek, his unmarried brother-in-law is Greek and therefore all the Germans must be married – two to each other and one to a British girl. Alternatively, if the American is married to a German, all the Greeks must be married. In either case the third American must be an unmarried female and therefore the second nun.

36

Inter-School Trophy

ANSWER

See table below.

SOLUTION

The possible winning margins are *12*, 10, 8, 6, 4, *2* = total 42. *One* of
these must be omitted and, as the schools ended equal in points, their
totals of winning margins are equal, and must be *even*. So the omitted
number must leave a remainder divisible by 4, i.e. it must be 10 or 6. If
10 is omitted, the total left is 32 (16 each); but then M's winning margin
in 1968 is 8, and they cannot make their total up to 16 in their other
winning year. So 6 must be omitted, and the remainder is 36 (18 each).
M had margin 10 in 1968, and must have made this up to 18 with a win
in the following year. So L won the cup in the other years.

A table may now be started, to be filled in progressively; the small
letters refer to the notes below.

	C 6	F 6	H 4	S 4	A 4	*Total* L	M
1967	L6d	L6d	M4d	L2M2d	L4a	18	6
1968	M6a	L3M3b	M4f	M4e	L4f	7	17
1969	L6b	M6c	L2M2a	M4c	M4c	8	16
1970	L6b	L6g	M4g	M4e	L2M2h	14	10
1971	L3M3b	L6g	M4g	M4e	L4g	13	11

a. Given in problem.
b. 1968; odd totals mean F drawn (3 each); so C draw was in other odd-
   total year (1971). So L won C in 1969–70.
c. 1969; L's total complete; so M won rest.
d. 1967; M at least 2 pts for S (L never won), and can't have 2 for H
   (draw 1969). Only answer is S2 H4.
e. S draw now fixed; M won in remaining years.
f. 1968; M's poorer record at A means only *one* win (1969) and one

draw (*not* 1968, where they need 4 pts). Their 4 pts must have come from H, and L won A.

g. 1971; M needs 4 more pts, which cannot come from F win, A win, or any combination including H draw. So M won H.

h. 1970; only year left for A draw. M then needs 4 more, which must come from H; so L won F.

37

Fallen Leaves

ANSWER

302 pages. The torn leaves are 75–6, 151–2, 301–2.

SOLUTION

This book must have an odd number of leaves, which can be torn out in three ways:

A. 1 leaf from the first half and 2 from the second half.
B. 2 leaves from the first half and 1 from the second half.
C. 1 leaf and a share of the middle leaf from each half.

It is required to find which of these deductions will yield the highest total of page numbers.

Let x = number of leaves ($2x$ pages). Then the total page numbers in the first half is $\dfrac{x^2}{2}+\dfrac{x}{2}$, and in the second half $\dfrac{3x^2}{2}+\dfrac{x}{2}$. These are brought into ratio $1:3$ by deducting thus:

1st half $\dfrac{x}{2}+(N)$ 2nd half $\dfrac{x}{2}+(3N)$.

A. The greatest number that can be taken from the first half is on the leaf preceding middle,

$$\text{i.e., pages } x-1 \text{ and } x-2 = 2x-3 = \frac{x}{2}+(1\tfrac{1}{2}x-3),\ N$$

$$\text{So second half must lose } \qquad \frac{x}{2}+(4\tfrac{1}{2}x-9),\ 3N$$

$$Total \quad \overline{7x-12}$$

B. The greatest number that can be taken from the second half is on the last leaf,

$$\text{i.e., pages } 2x-1 \text{ and } 2x = 4x-1 = \frac{x}{2}+(3\tfrac{1}{2}x-1),\ 3N$$

So first half must lose $\dfrac{x}{2} + (1\tfrac{1}{6}x - \tfrac{1}{3})$, N

$$\text{Total} \quad 5\tfrac{2}{3}x - 1\tfrac{1}{3}$$

C. The greatest number that can be taken from the second half is on the last leaf, plus share of middle leaf,

i.e., pages $2x-1$, $2x$ and $x+1 = 5x = \dfrac{x}{2} + (4\tfrac{1}{2}x)$, 3N

So first half must lose $\dfrac{x}{2} + (1\tfrac{1}{2}x)$, N

$$\text{Total} \quad 7x$$

So in order to produce the required effect, the greatest fall-out from *any* book of x leaves is the total $7x$.

Wherefore in this book $7x$ must lie between 1050 and 1070, and must moreover be odd;

so $7x = 1057$, therefore $x = 151$ leaves (302 pages).

38

Sharing Sweets

Mary was seven years older than Ann.

Clearly, we have to find seven fractions of the form $1/n$ whose sum is 1.

Now, it is easy to verify that

$$\tfrac{1}{3} = \tfrac{1}{4} + \tfrac{1}{12}$$
$$\tfrac{1}{6} = \tfrac{1}{9} + \tfrac{1}{18} = \tfrac{1}{10} + \tfrac{1}{15}$$

So $1 = \tfrac{1}{3} + \tfrac{1}{3} + \tfrac{1}{3}$
$= \tfrac{1}{3} + (\tfrac{1}{4} + \tfrac{1}{12}) + (\tfrac{1}{6} + \tfrac{1}{6})$
$= \tfrac{1}{3} + \tfrac{1}{4} + \tfrac{1}{12} + \tfrac{1}{9} + \tfrac{1}{18} + \tfrac{1}{10} + \tfrac{1}{15}.$

These are the only seven such fractions whose sum is 1.

The ages are 3, 4, 9, 10, 12, 15, 18.

The number of toffees is a common multiple of these, i.e. 180 or a multiple of 180. So the children received respectively 60, 45, 20, 18, 15, 12, 10 or their multiples.

But none of the multiples is 18. So Mary is 10, but Ann is 3, i.e. Mary is seven years older than Ann.

39

Bell's Weights

The weights are 4, 6, 9, 19, 38 giving 1 to 64.

See the note on Solution 29.

40

Logical Will

ANSWER

Thomas has £5000, Stephen £4000, Maurice £3000, Alec £2000, and Nigel £1000. Maurice may sing at the funeral service.

SOLUTION

1. The will contains four main sentences and three subordinate clauses. Therefore one sentence must stand alone and unqualified. Which?
2. Assume for the moment that it is the first ('M is not to sing at my funeral'), and therefore divide the rest of the will into three sentences *preceded* by subordinate clauses. Then we must *either* award A £5000 and S £3000 (but then the last sentence requires T to have £1000, whereas the second sentence requires him to have more than M, since A's £5000 cannot be exactly twice what N gets) *or* say that A does not have £5000 and S does not have £3000 (but then we get more than one possible solution, which Uncle George would not have allowed).
3. If we make the second main sentence ('A is to have £5000') the unqualified statement, we find the same difficulty. This is true also of the last sentence ('S is to have £4000'). In neither case is there one distribution and one only that will satisfy the conditions.
4. We therefore read the will as follows:
   'M is not to sing at my funeral, if S receives the £3000. A is to have £5000, if T gets less than M. A is to have twice what N has. If T does not receive the £1000, S is to have £4000.'
   Now *either* A has £4000 and N £2000 *or* A has £2000 and N £1000.
   If A has £4000, T has £1000 (since S cannot have £4000); but then T will have less than M, and A must have £5000 which is impossible.
   Therefore A has £2000 and N £1000. So S has £4000 (since T is *not* receiving £1000). So T gets £5000 and M £3000 (since A would have to have £5000 if T got less than M). This is the only solution allowed by this reading of the will, and it must therefore be what Uncle George intended.

180

41

Betting Prices

ANSWER

£71. 3 to 1; 6 to 1; 13 to 1; 20 to 1; 27 to 1.

SOLUTION

1. Each bet had to be such that, if the horse won, the amount recovered (i.e. stake plus winnings) would be the same.
2. We require an amount (say x) under £113 which, *inter alia*, has at least 5 factors between 3 and 29 (inclusive). Each of the 5 factors when divided into x would produce one of the stakes.
3. x will equal the sum staked on the 8 'paired' horses (an even figure) plus the stake on the favourite, plus £13. x cannot therefore be an 'odd' figure (if x were odd no factor of it could yield an even stake for the favourite – and an even stake on the favourite would be required to make x odd!).
4. x must therefore be an even figure under £113 but not less than £38 (minimum bets of £1, £2, £3, and £4 each multiplied by 2, plus £5 minimum for the favourite, plus £13).
5. The lowest of the 5 factors must be one which produces an 'odd' stake (for the favourite).
6. Possible numbers and relevant factors are:

   60 (factors 4, 5, 6, 10, 12, 15, 20)
   72 („   8, 9, 12, 18, 24)
   84 („   4, 6, 7, 12, 14, 21, 28)
   90 („   6, 9, 10, 15, 18)
   100 („   4, 5, 10, 20, 25)
   108 („   4, 6, 9, 12, 18, 27).

7. Close examination will show that only when $x = £84$ can a satisfactory arrangement be made, i.e. as follows:

Factor	Odds	Stake
1. 4	3 to 1	£21 favourite
2. 7	6 to 1	12
3. 7	6 to 1	12
4. 14	13 to 1	6
5. 14	13 to 1	6
6. 21	20 to 1	4
7. 21	20 to 1	4
8. 28	27 to 1	3
9. 28	27 to 1	3

Winnings plus stake in each case = £84.

£71
13 winnings
——
£84 = x.

42

Jacob's Ladder

SOLUTION

In order to attain maximum height on the wall, either ladder must clearly be positioned so as just to touch the top edge of the garage; we are therefore dealing with three similar right-angled triangles shown here as ABC, ADF, and CEF where $BC = BD = CE = 120$ inches.

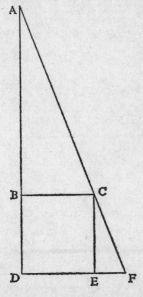

Now all measurements are known to be integral numbers of inches; thus these triangles must, in each instance, have sides whose lengths (numbered in inches) represent one particular multiple of the same basic Pythagorean group a, b, c (where $a^2 + b^2 = c^2$). This means that both a and b have to divide exactly into 120 (inches), and the only basic Pythagorean groups which satisfy this requirement are 3, 4, 5; 5, 12, 13; and 8, 15, 17.

We can now identify the following respective values:

Group	AB	$AD (= AB + 120\ in.)$	AF
3, 4, 5	$\frac{4}{3} \times 120 = 160$ in.	280 in.	$\frac{5}{4} \times 280 = 350$ in.
5, 12, 13	$\frac{12}{5} \times 120 = 288$ in.	408 in.	$\frac{13}{12} \times 408 = 442$ in.
8, 15, 17	$\frac{15}{8} \times 120 = 225$ in.	345 in.	$\frac{17}{15} \times 345 = 391$ in.

The first can be rejected since 350 inches is *not* over 30 feet. Thus clearly Jacob's ladder must be 442 inches long and Joseph's 391 inches (difference 51 inches), and reach 408 inches up the wall as against Joseph's 345 inches (difference 63 inches).

43

Some Sticky Impedimenta

ANSWER

D played 1 match, not 4. The scores were:

A v. B   0–0   B v. C   1–0
A v. D   0–3   B v. E   0–0
A v. E   2–1   C v. E   1–0.

SOLUTION

1. The figure which is wrong must clearly be found first. If D played 4 (i.e. played everyone), drew 0 and had 0 goals against, then they must have won all their matches and B cannot have had 0 goals against. So either D Pl or D Drawn or D Against or B Against must be wrong. So all other figures are correct.

2. C had 1 goal for and 1 against and drew 0; so C only played twice (scores: 1–0 and 0–1).

3. A had 3 points from 3 matches, but did not draw them all (see goals). So A won 1, lost 1, drew 1.

4. E only got 1 point, so won 0, drew 1, and played 3.

5. Thus, A, B, C, E played respectively 3, 3, 2, 3 matches. So D must have played an odd number (1 or 3) to make total played even. So the other figures are correct, and neither B nor D can have lost a match.

6. So we have:

	P	W	L	D	For	Against	Points
A	3	1	1	1	2	4	3
B	3		0			0	
C	2	1	1	0	1	1	2
D	1 or 3		0	0		0	
E	3	0	2	1	1		1

7. If D played 3, then the total number won would be greater than total number lost, which is impossible. So D played 1.

Therefore D played is the incorrect figure. It should be 1.

44

Family Birthdays

Saturday, 7 November 1964.

SOLUTION

1. It is necessary to find a set of nine days after the end of February which have the same day of the week in any one year, whether expressed in the English or American style, at least two of which must be of the form 3.3 (3 March). Reference to a calendar shows that this can happen to only one set:

   4 April, 9 May, 6 June, 11 July, 8 August, 5 September, 10 October, 7 November and 12 December.

2. The birthdays actually described by the problem are:

4 April	third son	
9 May	eldest son	attributed to me
6 June	eldest grandson	
11 July	?	attributed to my wife
5 September	me	
7 November	my wife	

3. The year 1964 had no significance, being only the year of composition. Similarly there is no significance in the fact that the third son was the birthday boy on 4 April. That was the survivor from a more elaborate version of the problem, in which the years of birth were also to be found out.

186

45

Triangular Bridge

ANSWER

C2 and A4.

SOLUTION

1. After each rubber player 3 or player 4 at each table moves clockwise, and player 1 or 2 moves counter-clockwise. Each player moves alternately depending on whether North/South win or lose.

2. Although their seating at tables other than their own may vary depending on whether the first rubber is won or lost, all the players will return to their original seats after the sixth rubber is played. The seating for the seventh rubber is therefore the same as that for the first rubber.

3. We are told that the eighth rubber at Table C is played with A1 in the North seat. It follows that:

   at Table A, North/South *lost* the seventh rubber;
   at Table C, North/South *lost* the seventh rubber.

   It is necessary to establish the possible movements at Table B.

4. When North/South lost the seventh rubber at Table A, player A4 moved to Table B to occupy the seat vacated by the winning player:

   (a) if North/South *won* at Table B this is seat B3;
   (b) if North/South *lost* at Table B this is seat B4.

   Similarly, the loser at Table C (C1) moves to occupy at Table B either (a) B2 or (b) B1.
   The partners for the eighth rubber are therefore either:

   (a) North/South B1–A4   East/West C1–B4 *or*
   (b) North/South C1–B3   East/West B2–A4

5. If the seating is at (a) North/South *won* the seventh rubber and must *lose* the eighth. Players B1 and B4 must move.
   If the seating is at (b) then North/South *lost* the seventh rubber and must *win* the eighth. Players B2 and B3 must move.

6. The partners for the *ninth* rubber are therefore either:

(a) North/South C2–A4   East/West C1–A3 *or*
(b) North/South C1–A3   East/West C2–A4

If the position is (a) then North/South *lost* the eighth rubber and must win the ninth; if (b), North/South *won* the eighth rubber and must lose the ninth. In either case the winning partners are C2 and A4.

46

Catering Crisis

ANSWER

80 sausage rolls and 72 pies; £2·36.

SOLUTION

The caterer must buy s sausage rolls, where s is between 100 and 50, and m pies, where m is between 90 and 60.

He spends 600p; so $3s + 5m = 600$ (a)

His takings will be:

	Sold		Disposed of	
	s.rolls	pies	s.rolls	pies
	at 4p.	at 8p	at 2p.	at 3p.
CClub	$4s$	8×60	0	$3(m-60)$
DClub	4×50	$8m$	$2(s-50)$	0

Total takings:

if CClub comes $4s + 3m + 300$ pence

if DClub comes $2s + 8m + 100$ pence

The values of s and m must be chosen so that these two totals are *equal*; otherwise, if the caterer guesses wrongly which club is coming, his takings will be less.

Therefore $4s + 3m + 300 = 2s + 8m + 100$

$$2s - 5m = -200$$
$$3s + 5m = 600 \quad \text{(a) above}$$

Add $5s = 400$

$$s = 80; \text{thus } m = 72.$$

Profit $4s + 3m + 300 - 600(\text{cost price})$ pence

     $= 320 + 216 - 300$ pence

     $= 236$ pence

     $= £2·36.$

47

Silver Collection

ANSWER

66s. 6d. and 69s. 6d.

SOLUTION

Using 2 sevens and 3 smaller numbers, there are five ways to obtain 27 coins. The correct selection is 7, 7, 6, 4, 3, this being the only one that gives the same sum of money from 5 permutations, i.e. 66s. 6d., with 69s. 6d. being the only higher sum obtainable twice.

For check if required:

Sixpences	Shillings	Florins	Half-crowns	Crowns	
3	7	4	6	7	= 66s. 6d.
4	3	7	7	6	,,
3	6	7	4	7	,,
4	6	3	7	7	,,
6	3	4	7	7	,,
3	4	7	6	7	= 69s. 6d.
4	3	6	7	7	,,

48

Dancing Partners

ANSWER

Ida was Mrs Swan.

SOLUTION

Let the table

Q	T	P	R	S
A	B	C	D	E
a	b	c	d	e
H	F	G	J	I

be arranged so that a, b, c, d, e are the wives of A, B, C, D, E respectively and the sisters of B, C, D, E, A respectively.

Let A represent Mr Quayle (Q).

Then he danced with d and d is Jane. As Q was the only man to dance with his sister's husband's sister, B, C, D, E did not dance with e, a, b, c respectively.

So B danced with c

C	„	„	e
D	„	„	a
E	„	„	b.

As c was the only lady who danced with her husband's sister's husband, c must be Gladys. The only lady who could be Mrs Pigeon's sister is b so b is Florence and C is Mr Pigeon and E is Mr Swan. The last man D must be Mr Robin, so a must be Harriet. Therefore e is Ida. Therefore Ida was Mrs Swan.

49

Hare Hill

ANSWER

4.32.

SOLUTION

The speeds of both drivers have been so chosen that in each case the
time taken for 1 km. uphill and 1 km. downhill is the same as for 2 km.
on the flat.

The travelling time is 220 minutes and if the full trip is $2X$ km.

$$\frac{X+5}{35}+\frac{X-5}{36}=\frac{220}{60}$$

giving $X = 65$.

If the road is uphill all the way arrival time would be 4.42. Flat all the
way arrival would be 4.22. So 4.32 is at most 10 minutes out.

50

Logicians in Conference

ANSWER

23.

SOLUTION

1. A lie cannot be detected if only one man answers 'Yes'.
2. A lie cannot be detected if two men *consecutively* answer 'Yes'. The numbers could be 25 and 27.
3. A lie cannot be detected if two men *alternately* answer 'Yes'. The numbers could be 121 and 125.
4. Only if the first and fourth men answer 'Yes' or if three or four men answer 'Yes' is a lie indicated.
5. The secretary's offer is useless if three or four men answer 'Yes'.
6. But if the answers are 'Yes', 'No', 'No', 'Yes', and the secretary advises that all four are lying, then the answers become 'No', 'Yes', 'Yes', 'No', i.e. 23, 25, 27, 29.

51

Golf Scores

(a) 3, (b) 5, (c) 5, (d) 4.

SOLUTION

1. John's 19 points were scored at 13 holes. The highest number of holes at which he could have scored only one point per hole was 8, and the only manner in which his score could have been made up was either:

(a) Holes	Score	Total		(b) Holes	Score	Total
8	1	8		7	1	7
4	2	8		6	2	12
1	3	3		13		19
13		19				

or

2. The scores available to Tom and Gerry are thus:

(1) Holes	Scores	Total		(2) Holes	Scores	Total
8	4 & 1	40		7	4 & 1	35
4	2 & 2	16		6	2 & 2	24
1	3 & 0	3	*or*	5	3 & 3	30
5	3 & 3	30		18		89
18		89				

(3)				(4)		
7	4 & 1	35		7	4 & 1	35
6	2 & 2	24		5	2 & 2	20
or 1	4 & 2	6	*or*	1	4 & 0	4
4	3 & 3	24		5	3 & 3	30
18		89		18		89

3. Arrangements (2) and (3) can be dismissed – they would mean that both Tom and Gerry scored a point or points at every hole.

4. In (1), Tom could score points at 18 holes and Gerry at 17, but it is not possible to make a division giving a margin of one point between Tom's total (45) and Gerry's (44).

5. The only acceptable division is derived from (4), i.e.:

| Tom | | | Gerry | | |
Holes	Score	Total	Holes	Score	Total
4	4	16	4	4	16
5	2	10	5	2	10
5	3	15	5	3	15
4	1	4	3	1	3
18		45	17		44

52

Equal Marks

ANSWER

15 marks.

SOLUTION

Total marks obtainable are $5 \times 40 = 200$, and each boy aggregated half-marks, i.e. 100. Hence 100 has first to be sub-divided into five parts (a, b, c, d, e, in descending order of magnitude) in compliance with the stated conditions.

Clearly a exceeds 21 and, since e is stated to exceed 10, d must exceed 11.

Now $5(a+c) = 6(a+d)$ or $c = \dfrac{a+6d}{5}$.

One may now substitute increasing values for a and d within the limits imposed and find, by trial, permissible values for c (remembering that $a-c$ must be 2 or more).

It is soon seen that the only possible sub-divisions of 100 are:

a	b	c	d	e	Total
25	24	23	15	13	100
26	25	22	14	13	100
33	23	21	12	11	100

Two of these rows of figures must now be shuffled around horizontally to find, again by trial, in how many ways four of the columns can be made to provide the same total m and the remaining one n, where $4m+n = 300$ and n is accordingly a multiple of 4 (which must be within the range 84, i.e. $33+26+25$ – the highest possible – to 40 which is the lowest possible).

It will be found that there are only two ways, viz. where $n = 56$ and 64 respectively. Thus:

33	23	21	12	11		33	23	21	12	11
13	14	22	26	25	*or*	13	26	14	22	25
15	24	13	23	25		13	15	24	25	23
—	—	—	—	—		—	—	—	—	—
61	61	56	61	61		59	64	59	59	59

and since the second-highest mark (26) is stated to have been obtained by Dick in the *maverick* subject, the first set of figures is invalidated. Now Tom was the top-mark scorer with 33; thus Harry got 15 marks.

53

The Un-Flats

ANSWER

Askew is a Pukka and lives at flat number 28. Bent is a Wotta-Woppa and lives at number 7. Crooked is a Shilli-Shalla and lives at number 12.

SOLUTION

1. If B1 is true, then A1 is true and C2 is true. But this is not possible as one of them is a W-W whose statements are all false. So B1 is false.

2. A1 and C2 cannot both be false, since one of the three is a Pukka whose statements are all true. So C2 must be true, and A1 may be true or false.

3. If C1 true then C is Pukka (two true remarks). But if C1 is true, C is Sh-Sh (nos. 11–20 are reserved for Sh-Shs). So C1 is false. So C is Sh-Sh, but does not live in number 18.

4. Neither B nor C is Pukka (they have both made a false statement). So A is Pukka, and both A's statements are true. So B is W-W, and B2 is false.

5. Since A2 is true, B lives at number 7.

6. And since A1 is true, A must live at number 24 or 28. But we know that A's number is not a multiple of 12 (B1 false), so A lives at number 28.

7. From B2 (false) C's number is a multiple of 6. But it is not 18 (C1 false). So C's number is 12.

54

Prime Flats

37, 37, 13, 7 and 7	Total 101
31, 31, 2, 2 and 1	Total 67
29, 29 and 1	Total 59
Grand total	227

SOLUTION

1. The number of primes between 24 and 40 is six. The number of families is 3 – 2 large prime numbers add up to an even number; 1 is excluded by reference to families always in the plural.
2. The oldest possible child is 13, born of parents both aged 37. This fixes the number of people in all families as the other 13.
3. The family sizes are 5, 5 and 3, which leaves three out of the four primes 1, 2, 7 and 11, each repeated once, as the ages of the rest of the children.
4. The total of the ages is prime – 227. This fixes the ages as 1, 1, 2, 2, 7 and 7. The rest is trial and error.

55

Stars

Eleven lieutenants.

SOLUTION

1. The total of officers present is a prime number.
2. Jeremy says that the total of the captains' stars (after counting heads) is ten more than the second-lieutenants' and twenty less than those of the full lieutenants. But Jeremy's total is one officer less than the real number of officers present, for Waffles was behind the bar. Therefore Jeremy's calculations are based on a number of officers *one less* than a prime.
3. These known facts can be tabulated:

Total officers	captains		lieutenants		2nd lieutenants		officers
(prime) (a)	stars (b)	men $\frac{1}{6}$	stars (b+20)	men $\frac{1}{4}$	stars (b−10)	men $\frac{1}{2}$	Total
11	12	2	32	8	2	1	11
17	18	3	38	—	8	4	—
23	*24*	*4*	*44*	*11*	*14*	*7*	*22*
41	42	7	62	13	32	16	36
47	48	8	68	17	38	19	44

As the party was 'small' it is hardly necessary to go further.

4. It will be seen that the total of 22 officers is the only number which fits Jeremy's observations; it is *two less* than the captains' stars he could see while being one less than a prime for the actual number of officers present. The statement that all the ranks are primes can only be true if Waffles is a captain. Therefore the number of lieutenants in the party was *eleven*.

56

What's My Age?

ANSWER

71.

SOLUTION

1. After reading my first three answers he must have been left with *two* numbers, one with an even digital root and one with an odd.
2. A study of the possibilities shows that this situation can arise from only one set of answers:

Under 55?

YES				NO			

Prime?

YES	NO	YES	NO
29, 31, 37, 41, 43, 47, 53	26, 28 . . . 54	59, 61, 67, 71, 73, 79	56, 58 . . . 78

Prime if digits reversed?

YES	NO	YES	NO	YES	NO	YES	NO
31, 37	29, 41, 43, 47, 53	32, 34, (30, 50)	Many	71, 73, 79	59, 61, 67	74, 76, (70)	Many

Dig. Rt

4, 1 *	Many	5, 7 (3, 5)	—	8, 1, 7	5, 7 4	2, 4 (7)	—

3. Only if my first three answers were YYY can he have been left with an alternative (*) bound to be resolved by my fourth answer. But my fourth answer cannot also have been Y, or no 'misleading transposition' is possible. So my answers were YYYN, whence he deduced my age as 37.

4. He was more than 20 years wrong; so I am over 55 and *should* have answered N to Q1. The correct answers were thus N Y Y Y, leading only to 71.

57

Ali's Counter Move

ANSWER

The counters are 2/4, 2/4, 2/4, 3/4.

SOLUTION

Baba commences with the counters:

1/2, 2/3, 3/4, 4/1, 1/3, 2/4

from which there is only one way to obtain 3 identical couplings with 2 strokes, thus:

1/2, 2/4, (3+1), 3/4, 4/2 (1+1), 1/3, 2/4.

   At Ali's call of 'Two', Baba plays 1/2, and at the call of 'One', he must of necessity play 1/3. The third call is again 'One' and he cannot fill it.

58

100-Yard Race

SOLUTION

Let a, b, c, d, e, f represent the numbers 1 to 6, e and f being the positions of the boys whose positions equalled each other's card-numbers.

Then $(a+b)(c+d)+2ef = 61$.

The possible values of $(a+b)$ and $(c+d)$ are odd numbers from 3 to 11 inclusive, so the possible values of $(a+b)(c+d)$ are

15, 21, 27, 33, 25, 35, 45, 55, 49.

The corresponding value of $2ef$ would be

46, 40, 34, 28, 36, 26, 16, 6, 12.
$ef = $ (23), 20, (17), 14, 18, (13), 8, 3, 6.

Inspection shows that the only possibility is

$$ef = 6 \times 1 \text{ and } (a+b)(c+d) = 7 \times 7$$
$$= (2+5)(3+4).$$

The table shows positions and numbers:

Position	1	2	3	4	5	6
Number	6	4	2	5	3	1
	L	H	K	O	N	M

59

Grand Vizier

ANSWER

1,393 tiles.

SOLUTION

The smaller square $x^2 = 2y^2 + 1$.
The larger square $a^2 = 2b^2 - 1$.
So both x^2 and a^2 are odd numbers and a^2 cannot exceed $44^2 = 1,936$.

The results are soon found by inspection. 9 tiles cannot be arranged as a central design and border (1 tile is not a design).

So Sultan's first square is $17^2 = 289 = 2 \times 12^2 + 1$, and his second square is $41^2 = 1,681 = 2 \times 29^2 - 1$.

He begins his second square with apparently only 288 tiles in hand and uses 1,681 tiles.

So he has taken an extra 1,393 tiles.

60

Lifts

ANSWER

13 floors.

SOLUTION

1. Let Black be x floors up.
2. So the lift which starts at the bottom (Lift A) travels x stages whenever the two lifts between them travel the full height of the tower. Therefore Lift A travels $2x$ stages between each meeting (as the two lifts between them travel twice the full height of the tower between each meeting).
3. So, since the third meeting is $x-4$ stages up the tower, the second meeting is $x+4$ stages up the tower (Lift A goes from $(x+4)$ to $(x-4)$ via the bottom).
4. As Lift A travels $2x$ stages in going from the floor where Black works to the top and from the top to floor $(x+4)$, it must travel $x+2$ stages from Black's floor to the top, and $x-2$ stages from the top to floor $(x+4)$. Therefore total height of tower $= 2x+2$ floors.
5. So the fourth meeting is at $(x+8)$ floor, the fifth is at $(x-8)$ floor, and the sixth is at $(x+12)$ floor.
6. So White's floor is $(x+12)$; but it is also $(2x+1)$ floor, as it is one from the top. Therefore $x = 11$. Total floors $= 24$.

61

Gold Cup

12, 19, 26, 33.

SOLUTION

1. If x were the lowest of the 4 non-runners and d the difference between each number and the next, the 4 would be x; $x+d$; $x+2d$; and $x+3d$ (total $4x+6d$).

2. The sum of the highest and lowest is thus $2x+3d$ (which is half the total of the 4).

3. The numbers of the first three horses in the race must therefore be:

   1st $\frac{2}{3}x$
   2nd $\frac{2}{3}x+d$ (one third of the total)
   3rd $\frac{2}{3}x+2d$
   Total $2x+3d$

4. The numbers of the 1st and 3rd must both be even (if $\frac{2}{3}x$ were odd, then x would not be a whole number). No. 15 must therefore have been second; the total of the first three horses $45(15 \times 3)$; and the total of the 4 non-runners 90.

5. x must be a multiple of 3, and possible arrangements are thus:

	x	d		x	d
(a)	3	13	(e)	15	5
(b)	6	11	(f)	18	3
(c)	9	9	(g)	21	1
(d)	12	7			

   ($2x+3d = 45$ in each case)

6. The only acceptable arrangement, it will be found, is (d), i.e.

$$x = 12 \qquad d = 7.$$

1st–3rd	Non-runners
1st $8(\frac{2}{3}x)$	12(x)
2nd $15(\frac{2}{3}x+d)$	19($x+d$)
3rd $22(\frac{2}{3}x+2d)$	26($x+2d$)
Total $\underline{45}(2x+3d)$	33($x+3d$)
	Total $\underline{90}(4x+6d)$

Note: Possibles (a), (b), (c), (f) and (g) are not acceptable because they would all include either 24 or 28 which are known to have been fallers. 'Possible' (e) is not acceptable because it would give 15 as second in the race and also as a non-runner.

62

Tennis Party

ANSWER

(a) 9 games; (b) none of them.

SOLUTION

It will be noted that all 6 names are applicable to either sex. The data indicate that P and F are of one sex and C and H of the other. The only uncertainty relates to S and E. But S and H cannot be of the same sex since both won *both* of their singles sets. Thus P, F and S are of one sex and C, H and E of the other. Now the only possible line-up for the three mixed doubles is

> P and H v. F and C (6–3)
> P and C v. S and E (4–6)
> F and E v. S and H (6–0 or 0–6).

But S and H cannot have *won* the third doubles, since both won their other doubles and both their singles and no one else could therefore have won the same number of games (24) as either of them. Hence F and E *beat* S and H 6–0.

H's total of won games is now seen to be 18, and it is impossible therefore for C, who won only 7 games in the doubles, to have won (in two lost singles) the required games to equal H's total. This floors solvers who (not unreasonably) assumed that Carol, Evelyn and Hilary were the girls.

But S's total of won games is also seen to be 18, and since P and F respectively won a total of 10 and 9 games in their doubles it is possible for each to have equalled S's total by having 8 and 9 games respectively in their singles (P losing 4–6 to both F and S, and F losing 3–6 to S).

Thus, playing against S, F won 3 games from *her* in the singles and later 6 games against her in the doubles – total 9 games.

Finally, it is clear that C's total of won games cannot exceed 15 (3+4+4+4), while E's is known to be at least 18 (3 won sets). Thus no player could have won 16 or 17 games.

63

The Lie Drug

A v. B   2–1
A v. C   1–1
B v. C   1–1.

SOLUTION

1. Since the number of matches won by A was not 0, and the number drawn by B was not 0, and goals for C were not 0, A, B and C all played at least 1 match.
2. No side can play more than 2. B has not played 1, so B has played 2.
3. A won 1 or 2 (figure given is 0), so A got at least 2 points. But figure given for A's points is 2, so A got more than 2 points, so A played 2. Therefore C must have played 2 (to make the total even), so they all played each other.
4. A's points must be 3 or 4; B drew at least 1 (figure given is 0). So B's points are 1, 2 or 3; so A and B between them got at least 4 points. Therefore C did not get more than 2 points (6 points altogether).

   C did not get 0 points (figure given) and C did not get 1 point (C did not draw 1, figure given), so C got 2 points, A got 3 and B got 1.
5. C did not win 1 (figure given), so C must have drawn 2. Therefore A v. C and B v. C were both drawn. And 3rd match (A v. B) was won by A (A got 3 points). We now know the result of each match.
6. Consider C's goals. The score in each of C's drawn matches was 0–0 or 1–1 (not more than 3 goals in any match). But not 0–0 and 0–0 (this would make 'Goals for' 0, but they are not). And not 0–0 and 1–1 (this would make 'Goals against' 1, but they are not). Therefore 1–1 and 1–1.
7. Consider B's goals. B scored 1 goal v. C, but more than 1 goal altogether (figure given is 1), therefore the score in B v. A was 1–2 (no other possibility).

64

Splat

Andrew played the last card, which was the 4 of spades.

SOLUTION

1. There were five players; each had four cards, one from each suit. The hands were:

	S	H	D	C	Order of play to first trick	Points
John	6	4	5	2	2	48
Dealer	2	6	4	3	1	37
	5	3	2	4	3	37
	3	2	6	5	4	35
Andrew	4	5	3	6	5	43

The tricks were:

Player	1	2	3	4	5	Won by	Points
	3C	5D	4C	5C	6C	Andrew	87
	4D	6S	5S	6D	5H	4	51
	6H	2C	2D	2H	3D	1	39
	2S	4H	3H	3S	4S	2	23

Player number 4 was second with 35 + 51 = 86 points.

2. Start by finding possible holdings for John:

S	H	D	C
6	4	5	2
5	4	3	2
2	6	3	4

3. Complete the matrix by fitting in the pairs of cards of the same value with the holding of one suit. (Clubs is quite a good suit to attack.) The matrix above is the unique solution.
4. In the play assume that Andrew's first trick is the highest possible. Hence the order of play is determined, and the remaining conditions can then be checked. It is not difficult to show that any lower score in the first trick is too low to top the second player's score.

65

Regatta

ANSWER

Seven minutes.

SOLUTION

1. The speeds of the boats were different whole numbers under 28 m.p.h. The times for their two-lap trials were in whole minutes.

2. The speed of each boat (in still water) being x m.p.h., its time over the ten-mile trial course in minutes is $\dfrac{600}{x}$ which is a whole number.

3. In the final race the adverse current was 5 m.p.h. As all but the slowest finished it may be assumed that the three fastest boats exceeded 5 m.p.h. Between 5 and 28 m.p.h., the only whole number factors of 600 are 5, 6, 8, 10, 12, 15, 20, 24 and 25.

4. The race as run was only five laps, three *against* the current and two *with* the current. The speed of each boat against the current is x minus 5, and the time for three laps is $\dfrac{900}{5-x}$. The time for the other two laps is $\dfrac{600}{x+5}$.

   Thus the required numbers of those given in (3) must also be factors of 600 (when plus 5) and factors of 900 (when minus 5). The only numbers which meet these conditions are: 10 (15 and 5); 15 (20 and 10); 20 (25 and 15); and 25 (30 and 20).

5. As the slowest boat dropped out we need consider only the three boats with the speeds of 15, 20 and 25 m.p.h. For the 10 miles of the trial laps, in still water, their times (and handicaps) were:

	Time	H'cap	for 30 miles
A. 15 m.p.h. for 10 miles	40 mins.	16	*48 mins.*
B. 20 m.p.h.	30	6	*18 mins.*
C. 25 m.p.h.	24	scratch	0

6. The starting and course times were:

Start	Time 3 laps	2 laps	Finish	
A. 11.12 a.m.	90	30	(120 mins.)	1.12 p.m.
B. 11.42 a.m.	60	24	(84 mins.)	1.06 p.m.
C. noon	45	20	(65 mins.)	1.05 p.m.

The difference between the winning and third boats is *seven minutes*.

66

Finger Trouble

ANSWER

E 5, H 7, I 8, J 9.

SOLUTION

Consider the denary (tens) equivalents of the two truthful answers: 242, 132.

Base	10	9	8	7	6	5	4	3
	242	200	162	128	98	72	—	—
	132	110	90	72	56	42	30	—

Only denary 72 agrees with both totals.

So Epo and Foto have 5 fingers each total		10
Gobo and Hingo have 7 ,, ,, ,,		14
Dojo has		10
Abo, Bunto and Coco have 4 each ,,		12
		46

This leaves 26 to be shared among I, J, K. None can have 10, and K has more than I. The only possible answer is I 8, J 9, K 9.

67

Here Comes the Bride

ANSWER

14 seconds. Chne is the bride.

SOLUTION

(a) Bud tells us that the centre floor line (c.f.l.) from den to stage is a determinate length.

(b) Bud's path is c.f.l. from den to junction with Chne. As this is geared to Chne's path it must be a determinate length and so therefore is the portion from junction to stage, i.e. all right-angled triangles used here have 3 determinate sides.

1. Ara drops a little to clear the beams, then runs 5 feet north, to clear the stage. She then drops to the floor. Her next leg is the exact feet hypotenuse of an integral right-angled triangle with base 16 feet. This offers (a) 16.12.20, (b) 16.30.34, (c) 16.63.65. Of these (a) is too short, (b) impossible for Chne, see below, so Ara uses (c). Her total journey is thus 70 feet run and 24 feet drop, which takes her to the north end of Bud's path, the den, in 62 seconds.

   Note: The c.f.l. is 63 feet.

2. The first leg of Chne's route is to the outer corner of the stage, 13 feet (5.12.13). The second leg is the exact feet hypotenuse of an integral right-angled triangle with base 28 feet. This offers (a) 28.21.35, (b) 28.96.100, (c) 28.45.53. Of these, (a) is too short, (b) too long, so Chne uses (c). Her total route is 66 feet in 72 seconds, which brings her to the south end of Bud's path. Bud's path is therefore 63−45 feet = 18 feet (216 inches) and as he was to have walked it in 72 seconds, his rate is 3 inches per second.

3. Ara has reached Bud's path 10 seconds sooner than Chne, and she runs 140 inches southward down the path by the time Chne arrives at the south end, so they are 216−140 inches = 76 inches apart.

   In another 3 seconds Chne runs 33 inches, Ara 42 inches = 75 inches. They are 1 inch apart. Wedding bells! But who is the bride?

4. If it is Chne, Bud has walked 216−33 inches = 183 inches. If Ara, 140 inches+42 inches = 182 inches. As he has walked exact seconds at 3 inches per second, Chne is the bride. Bud walked for 61 seconds. Chne for 75 seconds. Bud waited 14 seconds.

68

Birthdays

ANSWER

Ernest's birth-date was 10.3.28.

SOLUTION

The largest prime factor which can appear in the fifteen numbers is 7, for each date must contain a different multiple, i.e. 7, 14, 21, 28, 35. Hence, if 7 is a factor, so also is 5.

We also need 3 and 4.

Now $3 \times 4 \times 5 \times 7 = 420$ and this will not do, as $420 = 35 \times 2 \times 6$ or $35 \times 3 \times 4$, and 2, 6, 3, 4 must all be month-numbers.

So we must try 840.

Now 35, 28, 21 must be year-numbers and, as Charlie was nearly a year younger than David and as neither is the oldest or youngest, their years must be 21 and 20.

The other smaller factors are 2, 3, 4, 5, 6, 7, 8, 10, 12, 14, 15, so 2, 3, 4, 5, 6 are month-numbers, 7, 8, 10, 12, 14 are day-numbers, and 15 the lowest year-number.

Thus the dates are:

B   12.2.35 (only place for 2)
E   10.3.28 (,,   ,,   ,, 3)
C   8.5.21 (,,   ,,   ,, 5)
D   7.6.20 (,,   ,,   ,, 6)
A   14.4.15.

69

Ribbon Counter

Use a single E for the set of 6 11-inch spaces.

	1	1	3	5	5	5	E	6	6	1	1
and	20	19	18	15	10	5	E	6	12	13	14

is formed by adding the numbers to left (L) and right (R) away from E. If all the ten L and R numbers are each divided by 11 you have a different remainder each time; so you can make most measurements easily using Bell's 11-inch foot. The special arrangements to measure between 77 and 100 are well worth finding because many of them use both an L and an R with E. Try it!

70

Delphic Oracle

ANSWER

1965.

SOLUTION

1. If the largest computer was one of those that responded, it would have told Binary nothing; for both answers could be given by the largest computer whatever its date was.
2. Therefore the two smaller computers replied.
   The one which gave the first reply must have been
      either the 1960 computer (in which case the largest was 1965)
      or the 1965 computer (in which case the largest was 1960 or 1969).
   The one which gave the second reply must have been
      either the 1965 computer (in which case the largest was 1960 or 1969)
      or the 1969 computer (in which case the largest was 1965).
3. So the only possible arrangement is that the 1960 computer gave the first reply, the 1969 computer gave the second reply, and the date of the largest computer is 1965.

71

Air Ways

ANSWER

Al, Don, Ian.

SOLUTION

1. As Ian was going neither south (with Hal) nor east (with Gil) he must have been going north.
2. From A, B, C, D, E and F we require three pairs – one pair to go east with G; one pair to go north with I and one pair to go south with H.
3. From the text, a 'table' can be made as follows:

	Possibly with	Not with
A	D or C	B, E, F
B	—	—
C	A or E	B, D, F
D	A or C or F	B, E
E	—	—
F	B or E	A, C, D

4. As neither C (with A or E) nor F (with B or E) could be with D, the latter (D) must be with A. Thus C must be with E, leaving F with B.
5. As F was not going south and B not going north (with Ian), B and F must be going east (with G). As C was not going north (with Ian), he, with E, must be going south (with H) leaving A and D to go north with Ian, so that the full distribution is:

East – Bill, Fred, Gil.
North – Al, Don, Ian.
South – Cab, Ed, Hal.

72

Internationals

ANSWER

1–0.

SOLUTION

Scotland's performance provides the key to this puzzle. Let the total number of goals scored by them be x and the grand total by all in the Championship $2x$. Then since they (a) beat Ireland 3–1, and (b) earned only 3 points in all, they must have drawn one and lost the other of their remaining two matches and scored $(x-3)$ goals in doing so.

The lowest alternative scores in these two matches are therefore 0–0 and $(x-3)$–$(x-2)$ *or* 1–1 and $(x-4)$–$(x-3)$ *or* . . . etc., and the total of goals in *any* such case is $(2x-5)$. This, added to the 4 goals scored in the Scotland/Ireland match, accounts for a total of $(2x-1)$ goals and, since the grand total of goals was $2x$, only 1 goal was scored in all the remaining matches together. But England, with 5 points, must have won *two* matches; one of these must therefore have been against Scotland (who did lose one match), while the available 1 goal gives them their other win (at 1–0). Thus the score in the match between Ireland and the fourth country (Wales) can only have been 0–0 and, since Ireland's tally of points before (and after) the final match with Scotland was clearly 1 (earned from this draw with Wales), Ireland must have *lost* to England.

73

Dothemens Hall

ANSWER

Rachel's first remark was true. Priscilla's grade was D; Queeny's, B; Rachel's, A; and Susan's, E.

SOLUTION

1. Consider P2: if this is false, then Q's grade is A or B.

   Consider R1: if this is false, R's grade is D, E, O or F.

   Consider S2: if this is false Q's grade is lower than R's (it cannot be equal), i.e. Q's grade is E, O or F.

   But it is not possible for Q's grade to be A or B *and* to be E, O or F. So these 3 statements (P2, R1 and S2) cannot all be false, and so one of them must be true. Therefore all the other remarks made are false.

2. A diagram will help.

	A	B	C	D	E	O	F
P	X	X	X				X
Q	X						
R	√	X	X	X	X	X	X
S	X						

   From R2 (false), S's grade lower than P's; so S's grade not A, and P's grade not F.

   From Q1 (false) Q's grade not A; and from Q2 (false), P's grade not A, B or C. From P1 (false) someone got grade A, so by elimination R got grade A. (Information obtained so far has been inserted in diagram.)

3. We know that one of P2, R1, S2 is *true*. And we know that R1 is true (R's grade is A), so all the other remarks are false.

4. P2 is false, so Q's grade is A or B; but not A, for R's grade is A. Therefore Q's grade is B.

5. From R2 (false), S's grade is lower than P's. We know that P's grade is D, E or O, so S's grade is E, O or F.

6. From S1 (false), S's grade is E or higher, so S's grade is E, and P's grade is therefore D.

222

74

Catastrophe

ANSWER

It happened at 9.49 a.m.

SOLUTION

1. The answers can be represented by the matrix below:

	a.m.	15 to 45 minutes past hour	More than 3 hours from noon	Minutes past hour	Hands
Alf	Yes	Yes	Yes	45 to 50	
Bert	Yes	No	Yes		Right angles
Charlie	No	Yes		45 to 50	Coincident
Don		No		30 to 35	Opposite
Edward	No		No	15 to 20	Coincident

2. It is now simple to construct a 'truth table' assuming that any two of Alf's statements are true. Note that the assumption about column 2 affects the truth of column 4, and that only four different patterns for Alf have to be tested: TTFF, FTTF, TFFT and FFTT. Only one of these gives answers in column 5 for the other eye-witnesses, which are consistent:

Alf	T	F	F	T	
Bert	T	T	F		F
Charlie	F	F		T	T
Don		T	T	F	F
Edward	F		T	F	T

3. The rest is simple arithmetic.

75

Index Cabinet

SOLUTION

1. The capacity of the cabinet being 36×24, the average number of cards held by one initial must be less than 36. But the minimum number of cards must exceed 12×24 plus 23×13 or 587, an average of over 24. If the average is between 36 and 24 the initial with the average must include the drawer with less than 13 cards.

2. As there are twelve letters *below* the average there must be twelve initials holding different numbers of cards from 24 to 13. The total of this series is 222.

3. There must be twelve initials holding more than 24 cards. These must total a *minimum* of: 12 full drawers (288 cards) plus eleven of the series 13–24 (198 cards), or 486. Therefore there is a *minimum* total of over 708 cards, or an average of *over 29*. The *maximum* for these twelve initials is 288 plus 209 (222 less 13) plus the second drawer of the average letter (12) or 509. This gives a *maximum* possible total number of cards as 509 plus 222, or 731, which is an average per initial of *under 31*.

4. The average per initial must therefore be 30, and the total number of cards in the cabinet is 720.

5. As the average is 30 (one drawer plus 6), the eleven initials holding more than the average must have 720 minus 252 (222 plus the average), or 468. As the sum of the numbers between 37 and 48 is 510, the numbers to be discarded from this series to make the required total of 468 must be 24 and 18 (42).

6. As the middle column consists of full drawers, the first and third columns must hold the drawers containing 24 or less cards. The third column *must* hold the second drawers of all letters with over 24 cards, with one exception – the initial holding 48 cards, for in this case the 'second' drawer can either follow or precede the middle drawer. A

letter with only one drawer, in the third column, can only be in the same row as the letter with 48 cards.

7. The lowest possible total in the third column is therefore: the ten numbers 23, 22, 21, 20, 19, 17, 16, 15, 14, 13, and 6 or *186* plus the lowest 'single' (13) in the row containing two full drawers. The minimum total is therefore *199*, leaving space for *89* more cards.

76

Gouttes d'Or

ANSWER

NF 5.60.

SOLUTION

Call the volume of an olive x c.c.; thus it cost x centimes.

The *shape* of the brew is always conical; thus the volume is proportional to the (linear dimension)^3.

Originally there was $(\frac{4}{5})^3 \times 125$ c.c. $= 64$ c.c. liquor. Now there is $(\frac{3}{5})^3 \times 125$ *less* x c.c. $= (27-x)$ c.c. liquor.

Original cost price was 260 centimes; new cost 96 centimes.

Original cost *liquor* was $(260-x)$ centimes; new cost *liquor* is $(96-x)$ centimes.

So $\dfrac{64}{27-x} = \dfrac{260-x}{96-x}$; whence $64 \times 96 - 64x = 260 \times 27 - 27x$
$$-260x + x^2$$
i.e. $x^2 - 223x + 876 = 0$
$$(x-4)(x-219) = 0, \text{ whence } x = 4 \text{ (or 219, inadmissible)}.$$

The liquor therefore costs $\dfrac{260-4}{64}$ centimes/c.c. $= 4$ centimes/c.c..

If Gaston added the olive *after* measuring the liquor his cost price would be $27 \times 4 + 4$ centimes $= 112$ centimes.

To maintain 400 per cent profit he must therefore sell at *five* times this amount.

77

The Sheep Pen

ANSWER

13 11-foot pieces, 1 at 9 feet, 3 at 7 feet = 173 feet.

SOLUTION

First find dimensions of pen and length of longest fence piece. Omitting obviously impossible cases, we have:

	Dimensions	Common factor	Pieces used before check	Checked by Tom
(A)	99 ft × 440 ft	11 ft	50	2 (1 of 11 ft + 1 small)
(B)	110 ft × 396 ft	22 ft	24	28 (14 of 22 ft + 14 small)
(C)	,,	11 ft	47	5 (no half)
(D)	132 ft × 330 ft	33 ft	15	37 (no half)
(E)	,,	22 ft	22	30 (15 of 22 ft + 15 small)
(F)	,,	11 ft	43	9 (no half)
(G)	165 ft × 264 ft	33 ft	14	38 (19 of 33 ft + 19 small)
(H)	,,	11 ft	40	12 (6 at 11 ft + 6 small)
(I)	198 ft × 220 ft	22 ft	20	32 (16 of 22 ft + 16 small)
(J)	,,	11 ft	39	13 (no half)

So we have only to consider H. Tom loaded 46 11-foot pieces = 506 ft and 11 small pieces = 88 ft. Total 594 ft. To complete the east fence he has 7 at 11 ft + 6 small, i.e. insufficient.

He has three possible shorter constructions. They are:

1. Dismantle 8 11-ft pieces from the south fence. With 15 11-ft pieces and 6 small he has surplus fencing. *No solution.*

2. Dismantle 14 11-ft pieces from the south fence. Replace 10 ft (from small). With 21 11-ft pieces and (5)(4) small, he has surplus fencing. *No solution.*

3. At this point we require to find the lengths of the small pieces. (i) Tom loaded 11 small = 88 ft. (ii) Having lost 5 small, Tom is proposing to save 44 ft, so 5 small = 44 ft. (iii) So it is required to find how 88 ft can be distributed among 11 pieces of 3 different sizes, there being 1 only of the largest size. (iv) From this distribution it must be possible to detach 5 pieces totalling 44 ft, these 5 pieces to include the 1 largest piece.

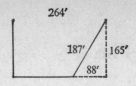

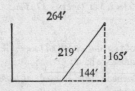

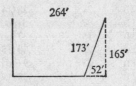

There are 6 possible distributions:

(a) 1 10-ft 7 9-ft 3 5-ft
(b) 1 10-ft 6 9-ft 4 6-ft
(c) 1 10-ft 9 8-ft 1 6-ft
(d) 1 10-ft 8 8-ft 2 7-ft
(e) 1 9-ft 9 8-ft 1 7-ft
(f) 1 10-ft 4 9-ft 6 7-ft

From (a) to (e) it will be found impossible to detach 5 pieces (including the largest) totalling 44 ft. This is possible only with (f).

Load 1 10-ft 4 9-ft 6 7-ft
Lose 1 10-ft 3 9-ft 1 7-ft
Use — 1 9-ft 5 7-ft

So Tom has 7 11-ft, 1 9-ft, and 5 7-ft in hand for the new east fence. He dismantles 6 11-ft from the south fence, replaces them by 2 7-ft and completes his new east fence with 13 11-ft, 1 9-ft and 3 7-ft = 173 ft.

78

Telephone Number

ANSWER

35742.

SOLUTION

Let the wife's age be a years, the son's b years and Fred's c years. The given facts may be summarized as follows:

(1) The telephone number is $1000a+100b+c$.

(2) $c-a = b$.

(3) The number is divisible by 259 or 7×37.

(4) a and c are each less than 70.

From (3), $1000a+100b+c$ is divisible by 7, but, from (2), $c = a+b$.

So $1001a+101b$ is divisible by 7;

but $1001a$ is divisible by 7,

so $101b$ is divisible by 7,

so $b = 7$.

Again, from (3) and using $b = 7$,

$$1001a+707 \text{ is divisible by } 37;$$

but $999a$ is divisible by 37,

so $2a+707$ is divisible by 37,

therefore $2a = 33$ or 70 or 107 or 144,

but $2a$ is even and less than 140.

So $2a = 70$

therefore $a = 35$ and $c = 42$, and the number is 35742.

79

Pints All Round

Using letters for players' numbers, the solution is

a b c d e f g
1 5 7 3 6 4 2

We are told a is 1 and is the first hit; and putting e = 6, g = 2 gives next 2 hits for 6 and 2. c cannot be 3, 4, or 5 else double hit with 1, 6 or 2 respectively, so c = 7. Similarly b is not 3 or 4, hence b = 5 and d is not 4 so d = 3 and finally f = 4.

80

Death of a Bishop

ANSWER

The murderer was Clym. He travelled six miles by train.

SOLUTION

1. Number the stations 0 to 9. The number of the station will correspond to its distance, in miles, from the Wessex terminus.
2. The total length of the morning rail journeys is $35(9+8+7+6+5)-10(4+3+2+1+0) = 25$. As the longest morning journey (Alec's) is 7 miles, the other four must have journeyed 6, 5, 4 and 3 miles in the morning. The same is true of the afternoon journeys.
3. The possible rail trips, all of different lengths and making use of all the stations, are these:

	7 miles (A)	6 miles	5 miles	4 miles	3 miles (C)
(1)	0–7	3–9	1–6	4–8	2–5
(2)	0–7	2–8	4–9	1–5	3–6
(3)	1–8	3–9	0–5	2–6	4–7
(4)	1–8	0–6	4–9	3–7	2–5
(5)	2–9	1–7	0–5	4–8	3–6
(6)	2–9	0–6	3–8	1–5	4–7

4. We now have to find two lines (one outward and one return set of journeys) which are different at all points and which allow two men to have a longer walk in Barsetshire than the others. Different at all points are (1) and (6); (2) and (3); (4) and (5). Of these, only the first pair gives two men longer walks than the rest.
5. Since Jude never turned his back on Wessex, the picture must therefore be:

	A	D or G	J	G or D	C
Outward	2–9	0–6	3–8	1–5	4–7
Return	7–0	9–3	6–1	8–4	5–2

The murderer (who left the morning train at station 7) is Clym.

81
Birthday Party

ANSWER

(a) Susan, Libby, Katie. (b) Sarah, Lucy, Cathy. (c) Sally, Lindy, Claire.

SOLUTION

1. The initial letters of the names were 3 Ss, 3 Ls, 2 Cs and 1 K. In two age groups, therefore, the initials would be S, L, C and in the third S, L, K.

2. As Sarah was older than Susan and Sally older than Lucy, both Sarah and Sally must have been older than six. Of the Ss, therefore, Susan must have been six.

3. As Libby was younger than Lindy and Lucy younger than Sally, both Libby and Lucy must have been younger than eight. Of the Ls, therefore, Lindy must have been eight.

4. As Susan was six, Libby was also six, and the third L, Lucy, must therefore have been seven.

5. As Lucy was younger than Sally, Sally must have been eight, and as Susan was six, Sarah must be seven.

6. As Cathy was not the same age as Susan (six) and Claire was older than Cathy, Claire must have been eight, Cathy seven and Katie six.

82

Grazing Rights

ANSWER

32 days.

SOLUTION

Let the sides of the two fields be respectively L and l yards. Then since 10 acres = 48,400 sq. yds, both L and l must somewhat exceed 220 yds, and $(L+l)$ must correspondingly exceed 440 yds.

Now $(L+l)(L-l) = L^2 - l^2 = 4,840$ sq. yds, and since $(L+l)+(L-l) = 2L$ both $(L+l)$ and $(L-l)$ must be even factors of 4,840.

Clearly the only values for $(L+l)$ and $(L-l)$ which satisfy the requirements are respectively 484 yds and 10 yds, so that $L = 247$ yds and $l = 237$ yds. Thus the area of the larger field is 247^2, i.e. 61,009 sq. yds, and that of the smaller is 237^2, i.e. 56,169 sq. yds (the difference being the requisite 4,840 sq. yds or one acre). The farmer should therefore be permitted to continue grazing 'for free' the 56,169 sq. yds for $\frac{4,840}{56,169} \times$ the previous agreed period of 366 days, or somewhat over $31\frac{1}{2}$ days.

Note: The reference in the puzzle to the year's grazing fee of £61 is both an irrelevance and a trap. It is tempting to figure that over 366 days this corresponded to 6 days' grazing for every £1 (forgetting that this relates only to the larger field) and that, since in the event it represents an overcharge of £4·84, the farmer should be allowed $6 \times 4·84$ additional days grazing, i.e. just over *29* days, whereas the correct answer is of course $\frac{61,009}{56,169}$ times that period.

83

Emblems Are Out

ANSWER

A, B and C are all Pukkas. A's number is 48, B's is 47, and C's is 46.

SOLUTION

1. Suppose B1 is false.
   Then A is W-W, so all A's statements are false. Therefore A3 is false, so C's 3rd remark is not true. Thus C1 is not true, C1 and C3 are true or false together), so A is a Sh-Sh.
   But this is contrary to our original assumption that A was a W-W. Therefore our assumption must be false, so B1 must be true.

2. Therefore B3 must also be true. So A must have 2 or 3 true remarks (A and B equally truthful), so A1 and A3 must both be true.

3. Since A3 is true, C's third remark is true, so C's first remark is also true. Therefore A is not a W-W (nor a Sh-Sh (C1)), so A is a Pukka.

4. From B3 (true), B must have 3 true remarks. Therefore C2 is true, so C4 is true. Thus we now know that all remarks are true.

5. Consider B2 and C3: from C3, C's number, *reversed*, must be 64, 32 or 16. And from B2, C's number is 2×a prime. But C's number cannot be 61 (too large), or 23 (a prime number, not twice a prime number). Therefore C's number must be 46.

6. From A2, A's number, larger than C's (see A1 and C4), and a multiple of 8, must be 48. And B's number (between A and C) must be 47.

84

Three Pairs of Twins

ANSWER

Albert Green	923 (13 × 71).
Betty Green	913 (11 × 83).
Charles Hall	943 (23 × 41).
Donald Hall	893 (19 × 47).
Ella Iver	901 (17 × 53).
Fay Iver	899 (29 × 31).

SOLUTION

1. The six lower numbers are 11, 13, 17, 19, 23 and 29. One pair is 29 and 31, whose product is 899. The other products are within 50 of this number.
2. The only other group of possible products is 901, 899, 983, 871, 869 and 851. In either case D, E and F have 901, 899 and 893 between them, and cannot tell which group is in use.
3. At stage 2 the Halls and Greens hold 901/869 and 899/871, or 923/913 and 943/893. In the first case the child (be he Hall or Green) holding 871 and the child holding 869 know the lot. In the second case the holders of 943/893 still cannot distinguish between 923 and 913, or between 901 and 899. The holders of 923/913 know all except the Ivers, and the Ivers know all except 923/913. The Halls are 943/893.
4. Albert Green holds one of 913/923, and wishes to distinguish between 901/899. If he holds 913, the answer will be 2 in each case, if he holds 923 it will be 1 or 2. This gives him away to all.
5. Similarly Ella is trying to distinguish between 913 and 923, and will only get different answers if she holds 901.
6. The Halls are boys. We can now fix the children's names. The children themselves, of course, know each other's names and are one step ahead of us at stage 4.

85

Badberg Clock

ANSWER

4 o'clock and 10 o'clock.

SOLUTION

1. The total loss of time due to the stops during the striking of each hour amounts in any twelve hours to the sum of the *intervals* in striking 2 to 12. There is no interval at 1. This sum is 66 times the pause between each stroke.
2. The clock is stated to be correct only at intervals of six hours. As the gain of the hands is constant they must gain the equivalent of 33 pauses every six hours. These hours must be the occasions when the constant gain is exactly offset by the preceding pauses.
3. The series of six consecutive numbers (under 12) which total 33 is from 3 to 8. These are the pauses which retard the hands between the striking beginning at 4 o'clock (three pauses) and the striking ending at nine o'clock (eight pauses). The only hours (six hours apart) at which the clock will begin striking correctly are therefore 4 o'clock and 10 o'clock.

86
Home Meadow

SOLUTION

Work in units equal to length of 1 fence-section. (This is permissible as p, r, s need whole numbers of sections, and, as will appear, so does x.)

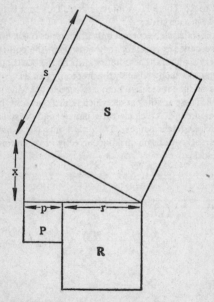

$s^2 = (p+r)^2 + x^2$; also $s^2 = 2(p^2+r^2)$

So $x^2 = 2p^2 + 2r^2 - p^2 - 2pr - r^2 = p^2 - 2pr + r^2$.

Therefore $x = p - r$ (or $r - p$, which fits the diagram).

Outer perimeter $= r - p + 3s + 2r + r - p + 2p$

$\qquad\qquad\qquad = 4r + 3s$, which $= 146$.

So $3s = 146 - 4r$, whence r is of form $(3n-1)$.

Possible solutions

r	$3s$	$2(p^2+r^2)$	p^2+r^2	p^2	p
2	138	46^2	1058	1054	No integral value
5	126	42^2	882	857	,, ,, ,,
8	114	38^2	722	658	,, ,, ,,
11	102	34^2	578	457	,, ,, ,,
14	90	30^2	450	254	,, ,, ,,
17	78	26^2	338	49	7
20	66	22^2	242	negative	—

Thus $r = 17$, $p = 7$, and so $s = 26$.

Common fences have total length $(p+r) + p + s = 24 + 7 + 26$
$$= 57.$$

87

National Anthem

ANSWER

138 notes.

SOLUTION

Call minims M, crotchets C, quavers Q, semiquavers S.

1. A convenient way to approach this puzzle is to treat S as a value unit, thus:

   M = 8S, a M dot = 4s, so a dotted M = 12s.
   C = 4S, a C dot = 2S, so a dotted C = 6S.
   Q = 2S, a Q dot = 1S, so a dotted Q = 3S.

2. There are equal numbers of M, C and Q. So we will call one of each MCQ a Group (G = 14S). Remember, a Group holds only plain notes at present. We shall have to provide 30 dots for them later.

3. The anthem measures 512S (32 bars at 16S). This is 36G+8S or 35G+22S or 34G+36S and so on.

4. Let us look at 36G+8S. Each G is 3 notes, so 36G is 108 notes. Now 30 of these have to be dotted, leaving 78 MCQ plain. But half the plain are semiquavers, so we must also have 78 plain S besides enough S to pay for the 30 dots, and we have only 8S for both jobs. It will be found that with any number of Groups down to 29G we shall have a shortage of S.

5. 28G+120S is 84 notes MCQ with 30 dotted and 54 plain MCQ, so we must have 54 plain S, leaving a surplus of 66S to allot as 30 dots to the group. The simplest way to allot shares here is by a simple trial and error.

6. Allot 10 dots to each member of the Group (in any case M and C must have the same). Then M gets 10 dots at 4S, C gets 10 dots at 2S, and Q gets 10 dots at 1S. Total 70S, which is 4 too many, so we try giving M 9 dots at 4S, C 9 dots at 2S and Q 12 dots at 1S = 66S, and so we have:

	M	C	Q	S		
Dotted	9	9	12	—	= 198S	
Plain	19	19	16	54	= 314S	= 512S
	28	28	28	54	= 138 notes.	

When this problem was published in the *Sunday Times*, some readers doubted whether a solution was musically practicable. Their doubts were quite brilliantly resolved by Mr Alan Hope, whose entry included the splendid martial theme printed below.

THE BAHREIN TEZA NATIONAL ANTHEM

MARZIALE

Alan Hope

88

Cross Country

Harry was 17th, wearing 3; Dick was 7th, wearing 11; and Tom was 5th, wearing 15.

SOLUTION

If a, b, c are the three position numbers and x, y, z the three card numbers, the sum of the 9 products is $(a+b+c)(x+y+z) = 841 = 29 \times 29$.

Therefore $a+b+c = 29$, and
$$x+y+z = 29.$$

The only triples of odd numbers totalling 29 are:

3	3	3	3	5	5	5	7
5	7	9	11	7	9	11	9
21	19	17	15	17	15	13	13

Since all 6 numbers are to be different, the only pairs of triples to be considered are:

3	7	3	5	3	5	3	5	3	5	3	7
5	9	7	9	7	11	9	11	11	7	11	9
21	13	19	15	19	13	17	13	15	17	15	13

not necessarily in corresponding order.

As Dick's position in the Junior race was greater than his card number and he beat the others, his card number must have been 3.

Therefore the card numbers must be a triple containing 3; but in the Senior race he wore the highest card number and this was smaller than his position number. This only happens in the pair 3, 11, 15 and 5, 7, 17 so we can now make a table showing results and cards of all 3 races putting position first, bearing in mind all numbers in the same row or column are different and no pair occurs twice.

	S	C	J	Product Totals
T or H	5.11	17.3	7.15	211
H or T	7.3	5.15	17.11	283
D	17.15	7.11	5.3	347

The top row has the smallest total and so corresponds to Harry.

Therefore in the Colts' race Harry was 17th, wearing 3; Dick was 7th, wearing 11; and Tom was 5th, wearing 15.

89

British Triangles

There are four kinds of triangles. The sides are (a) 15, 41; (b) 17, 25; (c) 17, 39; (d) 26, 30. The heights are (a) 9; (b) 15; (c) 15; (d) 24. Each produces 2 B.T.s.

See the note to Solution 29.

90

Logic Club

ANSWER

Briggs and Denby stood up. Crane owns the Rover.

SOLUTION

1. If Anstey's second statement were true, his first would be true also. So A's first statement is true and his second untrue. Therefore A owns T, V or W.
2. Briggs clearly owns either V or W.
3. If Denby's first statement were true, his second would be true also. So D's first statement is untrue and his second true. Therefore D owns R, V or W.
4. Crane's first statement could be true only if he owned either V or W. He would then know that B owned whichever of these two he himself did not own, and therefore that A owned T. *But* C would then stand up after D's statements, knowing that D owned R and therefore that E owned S. As C doesn't then stand up, his first statement must be untrue and he owns neither V nor W. As his second statement is true, he doesn't own T either. Therefore C owns R or S.
5. After D's statements (and C's failure to stand up), A would stand up if he owned V (knowing that BDCE owned WRST); he would also stand up if he owned W (knowing that BDCE owned VRST). But he doesn't stand up; so everyone knows that A owns T.
6. Now consider the position of E before he speaks. He has drawn all the above conclusions from the fact that nobody has yet stood up; so he would stand up if he owned V (knowing that ABDC owned TWRS) or if he owned W (knowing that ABDC owned TVRS). But he doesn't stand up; so everyone knows before he speaks that E does not own V or W, nor does he own T (which A owns). Therefore E owns R or S.
7. So E's first statement must be *true*, since he does indeed know that C's car is whichever of R and S he himself does not own. So E's second statement is untrue. So E owns S. Therefore C owns R.
8. Nobody can tell how V and W are distributed between B and D, except B and D themselves. So these two stand up.

91

Cash Crossword

ANSWER

A 4	B 1	C 6	D 3
E 6	3	F 1	0
1	G 6	6	1
H 1	I 7	J 1	1
K 1	9	4	4
L 1	7	9	5

92

Fairies in the Garden

ANSWER AND SOLUTION

The nearest black is 10 feet from the post, on the border either to the right or left. Put it to the right. The distances of the twelve fairies up the centre line and then right + or left − are

Black (0, +10) (12, −2) (60, 10)
Red   (12, +6) (12, −6) (15, 0) (20, 0) (20, +10) (20, −10) (30, 0) (60, +30) (60, −30)

Our nearest black could be to the left at (0, −10) and the other blacks at (12, +2) and (60, −10) the reds being unchanged.

'You couldn't possibly get more than 20'; no point can have more than 5 lines through it, i.e. 60 lines in all, but each line has been counted 3 times, so 20 is a maximum for any distribution whatever of 12 points.

Note: Graph paper is advised.

93

Pi Crater

SOLUTION

1. Let the distance travelled by the lizard in one hour be called 1 crawl, and the distance travelled by the lion in one hour be x crawls.

2.

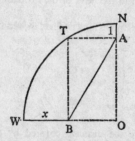

So AB (the path they would travel during the second hour in order to meet) is $\frac{3x}{2} + 1$ crawls in length.

3. But AB is the same length as OT, the radius of the reserve (diagonals of the same rectangle). So at A the lizard $\left(\frac{3x}{2}+1\right) - 1$ crawls from the centre at O. And at B the lion is $\left(\frac{3x}{2}+1\right) - x$ crawls from the centre at O. And these two are the sides of a triangle whose hypotenuse is $\frac{3x}{2} + 1$ crawls in length.

4. So $x = 8$; the triangle's sides are 13, 12 and 5; and the lion's path from west to east is 26 crawls long.

5. Doing 8 crawls per hour, the lion took 3¼ hours to cross the reserve.

94

People's Procession

ANSWER

$4\frac{1}{2}$ miles.

SOLUTION

Let the procession be moving forward at v m.p.h., while the speed of the patrolman is V m.p.h.; and let t_1 and t_2 be the times (in hours) taken by him to go from the tail to the head of the procession and vice versa respectively.

Now the procession is 2 miles long and had moved $1\frac{1}{2}$ miles;

hence $t_1 = \dfrac{2}{(V-v)}$ and $t_2 = \dfrac{2}{(V+v)}$.

Also $\dfrac{1\frac{1}{2}}{v} = (t_1 + t_2) = \dfrac{4V}{(V^2-v^2)}$

whence $3V^2 - 8Vv - 3v^2 = 0$

or $(V-3v)(3V+v) = 0$.

Therefore $V = 3v$, and the distance covered by the patrolman is $3 \times 1\frac{1}{2}$ miles, i.e. $4\frac{1}{2}$ miles.

95

Circular Tour

ANSWER

12 miles.

SOLUTION

Considering a round journey in one direction, from each village it is possible to go to five other villages; hence there are 30 different distances between villages. If we now include the whole circuit, there are 31 different distances. As every whole number from 1 upwards is to be used, the whole circuit is 31 miles.

There must be a 2-miles distance and, if it is adjacent to the 1 mile AB, it must be BC, for FA is greater than BC. By trial it is soon found that sequences 4–1–2 and 1–2–4 lead to no solution.

Deferring 4, try 1–2–5 and 5–1–2. To make 31, remembering that we still need 4, we must have two distances totalling 19. These must be 6 and 13, or 7 and 12, giving the two solutions shown:

```
   E 4 D                E 4 D
  6     5             12      7
F         C  (1)    F          C  (2)
 13     2             5      2
   A 1 B                A 1 B
```

Using 1–3–2, another possibility is:

```
   E 7 D
  8     2
F         C  (3)
 10     3
   A 1 B
```

Solution (2) alone makes EF greater than FA. Therefore EF is 12 miles.

96

The Poorer the Truer

ANSWER

A is a Sh-Sh (more truthful), his wages are £19 per week, and he is married to Z.

B is a W-W, his wages are £24 per week, and he is married to Y.

C is a Sh-Sh (less truthful), his wages are £20 per week, and he is married to X.

D is a Pukka, his wages are £16 per week, and he is a bachelor.

SOLUTION

1. Suppose C3 is true. (So C1 is also true.) B is thus more truthful (because wages are less). So B must make 3 true remarks, so B is Pukka. Therefore B2 ('I am a Sh-Sh') is false. But this is a contradiction, so our assumption must be false. Therefore C3 is false, and C1 must also be false.

2. Since C3 is false and wages are all different, B's wages are more than C's, so B is less truthful than C, so B's remarks all false, so C's remarks not all false, so C2 is true (we already know that C1 and C3 are false).

3. A diagram will help.

   A1 √   C1 ×
    2   2 √
    3 √   3 ×
   B1 ×   D1 √
    2 ×   2
    3 ×   3 √

   We see from this that either A or D is a Pukka (all remarks true) and the other one must be a Sh-Sh with 1st and 3rd remarks true. Therefore A1, A3, D1 and D3 are all true, and one only of A2 and D2 is true. (This information has been inserted in diagram.)

4. A diagram giving information about wives and wages will also help.

Wages		X	Y	Z	Bachelor
	A		X		
24, 30	B	X	√	X	X
	C		X		X
16, 20, 24, 28	D		X		

5. We know that A1 is true. So $\dfrac{\text{B's (W-W's) wages}}{\text{one of Sh-Sh's wages}} = \dfrac{120}{100} = \dfrac{6}{5}$.

Therefore B's wages are a multiple of 6, so they must be 18, 24, or 30. And thus one of Sh-Sh's wages must be 15, 20 or 25. But not 15, for this is lowest pay possible, so only a Pukka could have this pay. So B's wages are 24 or 30, and one of Sh-Sh's wages are 20 or 25.

6. From A3 (true) D's wages must be 16, 20, 24 or 28.

7. From B3 (false) B (W-W, best paid) is *not* married to X.

8. From D3 (true) B is *not* married to Z.

9. From C2 (true) the Pukka is a bachelor, so neither B nor C is a bachelor. Therefore by elimination B is married to Y. (The information so far has been inserted in diagram.)

10. From B1 (false) Z's husband's wages are odd, so Z's husband is *not* D.

11. Consider A2. Suppose this is true. Then B's wages must be 30 (not 24 for A's would then be 14 which is not possible). So A's wages must be 20. And from paragraph 5 if B's wages are 30 then one of Sh-Shs' is 25. But in this case wages are 20; 30; 25; 16, 20, 24 or 28; and D1 is false. But we know that D1 must be true. So our assumption is false and A2 cannot be true, so A is Sh-Sh and D is Pukka.

12. From D2 (true) the wages of the Sh-Shs differ by £1. From A1 (true) wage of one of Sh-Shs is £20 or £25. (See 5.) From D1 (true) someone's wages are a prime number of £s. But this cannot be B or D or one of Sh-Shs (£20 or £25), so it must be other Sh-Sh. But if wages of one Sh-Sh are £25, then wages of other would be an even number, and so not prime. Therefore wages of one Sh-Sh are £20 and of other £19. So the less truthful Sh-Sh (C) has wages of £20 and other (A) has wages of £19. So the wages of W-W (B) are £24. So wages of Pukka (D 16, 20, 24 or 28) can only be £16.

13. From C2 (true), D is a bachelor. From B1 (false), Z's husband cannot be C. So Z is married to A and by elimination C is married to X.

97

The ABC Club

ANSWER

I am an actor.

SOLUTION

1. If Q is B, then P tells the truth, and is either B or A. If Q is C, then P lies, and must be A. If Q is A, then P lies, and must be B. The possibilities for PQ are: BB, AB, AC, BA.

2. If Q is C, then R lies and is A. If Q is A, then R tells the truth and is A or C. If Q is B, then R tells the truth and is B or A.

3. Combining 1 and 2, PQR could be BBB, BBA, ABB, ABA, BAA, BAC, ACA. The first is inadmissible as there cannot be more than two of a kind.

4. R to P: 'You are either B or C.' P cannot be C (see 3 above). If PB, R truthful and either B or A (a). If PA, R lies and is B. If (a) then only BBA and BAA possible. If (b) then only ABB possible.

5. In all three cases above, S must be the missing C; S's remark to R: 'You are the same as P', cannot be true; so S(C) is addressing a B. Therefore PA, QB, RB, SC.

6. Look at the remarks made by three of P, Q, R, S for the three possibilities of *my* job:

	P	Q	R	S
I am A	A	B/C	B/C	A
I am B	B	B	B	A/C
I am C	A/B	C	C	C

Only if I am A can any three of P, Q, R, S, produce only *one* true statement.

98

Bouquet

Yellow.

SOLUTION

1. As the bouquet has equal numbers of each colour, the total is a multiple of a basic group containing one bloom of each colour.
2. Each neighbour has two colours and an equal number of each was taken from each garden. To complete the basic group an additional red and yellow must be taken from my garden, as there are from my neighbours 2 whites, 2 crimson, and only *one* red and *one* yellow.
3. *Cost*. From the given data the cost of each flower, taking a rambler as one unit, is:

Red rambler	1
White rambler	1
dwarf	$2\frac{2}{3}$
Crimson standard	$1\frac{1}{3}$
bush	$1\frac{1}{3}$
Yellow standard	$\frac{2}{3}$
Total	8 times one rambler

(My own speciality – colour unknown – is worth 4.)

4. To each total of eight (for six different roses) must be added the cost of one red and one yellow bloom from my garden (see para. 2). These may be either:

Red rambler plus yellow standard	cost $1\frac{2}{3}$
Red rambler plus yellow speciality	5
Yellow standard plus red speciality	$4\frac{2}{3}$

5. The total value of the bouquet being 26, this must be a multiple of either (8 plus $1\frac{2}{3}$) or (8 plus 5) or (8 plus $4\frac{2}{3}$), that is, either $9\frac{2}{3}$, *13*, or $12\frac{2}{3}$. Only *13* will suit, and therefore two flowers of each colour were taken from each neighbour's garden (cost 16) and from my garden 2 red ramblers (2) and two specialities (8) which must be *yellow*.

   (It is, in fact, a yellow dwarf.)

99

Tessie the Typist

ANSWER

1,238,769.

SOLUTION

1. Any odd number when squared produces a number ending in 1 or 5 or 9.

2. Y (like X) must be smaller than the number typed in its stead. The first digit in Y must, therefore, be 1 and the last 9.

3. As the digit total of Y was over 35, Y could not run to less than seven figures (the maximum for six would be 35 – i.e. 1 4 6 7 8 9) or more than eight – i.e. 1 2 3 4 6 7 8 9.

4. X must, therefore, be a four-figure number.

5. A last figure of 9 can only be produced by squaring a number ending either in 3 or 7, and a last figure of 1 can only be produced by squaring a number ending either in 1 or 9.

6. X and the number typed in its stead must, therefore, have been either (a) 1,..3 and 3,..1; or (b) 9,..3 and 3,..9; or (c) 1,..7 and 7,..1; or (d) 9,..7 and 7,..9.

7. Since X was smaller than the number typed in its place, (b) and (d) are unacceptable. Moreover, since no four-figure number beginning with 7 can have as its square a number beginning with 9, (c) also can be ruled out.

8. We are left with (a) 1,..3 and 3,..1. The square of 1,..3 cannot run to more than seven figures and the square of 3,..1 must, therefore, similarly be limited to seven figures. The highest number which, when squared, does not exceed seven figures is 3,162. Thus the only possibilities are:

(i)   1,113 and 3,111
(ii) 1,213 ,, 3,121
(iii) 1,313 ,, 3,131
(iv) 1,413 ,, 3,141
(v)   1,613 ,, 3,161

9. Only (i) will be found to meet requirements, i.e. $X = 1,113$ and $Y = 1,238,769$ $(1,113^2)$, and Tessie typed 3,111 and 9,678,321 $(3,111^2)$.

100

Good-bye

3,276.

The 3 smaller numbers must be in ratio $1:7:28 = 36$. ($1:5:30 = 36$ is ruled out as involving zero.)

That is to say, we multiply the two-figure number by 7 to obtain the three-figure number, which multiplied by 4 gives the four-figure number.

The two-figure number cannot be less than $3,000 \div 36 = 84$ approx. So, omitting numbers ending in 5 or 0 (which involve zero), and double-figure numbers, we have *84*, *86*, *87*, 89, 91, *92*, 93, 94, 96, *97*, *98*. Multiplying these by 7 eliminates those italicized, and we now have *623*, 637, *651*, *658*, *672* as possibles for the three-figure number. Multiplying by 4 eliminates those italicized, leaving only 637, and the 3 smaller numbers are 91, 637, and 2,548, totalling 3,276.

101

Spot the Setter

91 W.M.G.
92 W.A.T.
93 B.W.M.Y.
94 G.H.D.
95 J.S.R.
96 E.R.E.
97 R.P.
98 J.J.
99 J.L.B.
100 C.S.Q.

Postscript:
Adrian Winder's Problem

(Sunday Times Brain Teaser 186, 15 November 1964)

A is 73 feet from a straight river, and B is on the same side of the river but not so far from it. M and N are the (distinct) points on the river nearest to A and B respectively. The lengths of AB, MN, and BN are whole numbers of feet.

A man walks from A to B via the river, taking the shortest possible route, and this is also a whole number of feet.

How far does the man walk, and what is the direct distance from A to B?

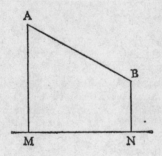

Brain Teaser 186

169 feet; 123 feet.

SOLUTION

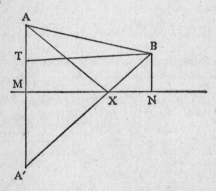

A' is the reflection of A in the river, and $A'B$ meets MN at X. Then
$A \rightarrow X \rightarrow B$ is the shortest route, and its length is $A'B = x$, say. Let
$AB = p$, $AM = a$, $BN = b$, $MN = d$. T is the foot of the perpendicular from B to AM.

Then $x^2 = A'B^2 = BT^2 + A'T^2 = d^2 + (A'M + MT)^2 = d^2 + (a+b)^2$
and $p^2 = AB^2 = BT^2 + AT^2 = d^2 + (a-b)^2$.

Writing $a+b = h$, $a-b = k$, we have
$$x^2 = d^2 + h^2$$
$$p^2 = d^2 + k^2, \text{ where } h + k = 2a = 146.$$

Of the 72 possible pairs of h and k, namely (145, 1), (144, 2) ...
(74, 72) only (119, 27) allows these equations to be solved in integers,
and moreover the solution is unique. In fact, $169^2 = 120^2 + 119^2$ and
$123^2 = 120^2 + 27^2$.

More about Penguins and Pelicans

Penguinews, which appears every month, contains details of all the new books issued by Penguins as they are published. From time to time it is supplemented by *Penguins in Print*, which is a complete list of all available books published by Penguins. (There are well over four thousand of these.)

A specimen copy of *Penguinews* will be sent to you free on request. For a year's issues (including the complete lists) please send 30p if you live in the United Kingdom, or 60p if you live elsewhere. Just write to Dept EP, Penguin Books Ltd, Harmondsworth, Middlesex, enclosing a cheque or postal order, and your name will be added to the mailing list.

Note: *Penguinews* and *Penguins in Print* are not available in the U.S.A. or Canada

The Daily Telegraph Tenth Crossword Puzzle Book

Compilers of the *Daily Telegraph* crosswords seem to understand (bless their bones) that a successful reader is a satisfied reader. Eight hours of concentration at the office are generally sufficient to break the backs of their puzzles ... and who, having got that far, will resent taking work home in the evening?

Occasionally, of course, even these paragons are moved by some dark, sadistic impulse: rivers, in their momentarily twisted language, become flowers or bankers ... or they light, with their intellectual forceps, lovingly on some quotation which (and they well know it) is not in the appropriate Penguin dictionary, let alone the Oxford one.

However, such lapses are rare. On the whole the *Daily Telegraph* in its crosswords, neither daunts nor coddles the reader. It caters very fairly for that Abominable Snowman of sociology, the average man: we mean, in this case, the man who is too balanced to read more than the headlines of the news, too creative to remain a mere reader all day, too secure to study the excellent advertisements of vacancies, and too lethargic to open the paper.

The 100 crosswords in this volume have cost others £1.66½. At our price they are a bargain.

Also available

The Daily Telegraph Eleventh Crossword Puzzle Book

The Penguin Book of Ximenes Crossword Puzzles

The Penguin Book of Financial Times Crosswords

The Listener Crossword Puzzle Book (Two vols)

The Scotsman Crossword Puzzle Book